CW00346217

To Be A Neurosurgeon

Author's wife Sheelagh (oil on canvas, Raeburn Dobson)

TO BE A NEUROSURGEON

A Memoir

by

PHILLIP HARRIS

The Memoir Club

© Phillip Harris 2009

First published in 2009 by
The Memoir Club
Arya House
Langley Park
Durham
DH7 9XE
Tel: 0191 373 5660
Fax: 0191 373 9652
Email: memoirclub@email.msn.com

British Library Cataloguing in
Publication Data.
A catalogue record for this book
is available from the
British Library

ISBN: 978-1-84104-137-7

Typeset by TW Typesetting, Plymouth, Devon
Printed by Cromwell Press Group

To my dear wife, Sheelagh, who for nigh on 60 years has shared with me our joys and sorrows of life.

Contents

List of Illustrations

Foreword

Phillip Harris has written a unique and personal account of an interesting life that now spans some eighty-six years. Born, schooled and trained in Edinburgh he graduated from its renowned medical school in 1944, serving in the RAMC from 1945–48. He had the privilege of a ringside seat during key stages of the development of neurosurgery in Edinburgh and provides fascinating insights into the work and life of his great mentor Professor Norman Dott. Appointed as a consultant neurosurgeon in his native city he worked alongside Dott and that other Edinburgh giant, John Gillingham, and describes the move of Edinburgh neurosurgery to the Western General Hospital and into the first custom-built department of neurosurgery in the UK.

This is no conventional memoir. It will have great interest for professional readers in that the author has travelled widely in pursuit of excellence, met many of the great figures of his and related disciplines, and was never confined by rigid boundaries. His diplomas (FRCSEd, FRCPE, FRCS [Glas] and FRSE) attest the breadth of his training and interests. His reminiscences will make fascinating reading for those interested in the history of the Edinburgh medical school and the technical advances in neurosurgery. The lay reader will also value the readable background information that will allow fuller understanding of the many case histories that the author uses to illustrate the breadth of his lifetime experience of his discipline. His curiosity has not been confined to neurosurgery, however, and forays into the modern field of stem cell research and thoughts of Rembrandt as an anatomist or Mahler as a composer will also make for interesting reading.

Neurosurgery has benefited greatly from the contribution of Phillip Harris and there can be no doubting his particular contribution to the strength of neurosurgery and related neurosciences in Edinburgh. He writes with the authority of one who worked extensively at the growing edge of his specialty, who has engaged internationally with all that is best in his field, and who has made numerous scholarly contributions to neurosurgery and in particular to our understanding and management of disorders of the spinal cord.

There is great warmth in this memoir and its description of family, friends and colleagues. Phillip Harris has decided to sit down late in life and compile an invaluable account of his experiences of neurosurgical life and life in the Edinburgh medical school. I commend him for doing so and recommend his memoir unreservedly.

Sir David C. Carter FRSE
Chairman of the Health Foundation
Chairman of the Board for Academic Medicine in Scotland

Preface

Once upon a teatime our young grand-daughter, Abigail, turned round to me and asked: 'Grandpa, what does a neurosurgeon do?' This set me thinking; my short answer was: 'A neurosurgeon is a medical doctor specially trained to have a detailed knowledge of the nervous system, the brain, head, spine, spinal cord and the nerves, so that diseases or injuries of the nervous system can be diagnosed, and if and when indicated, treated by a neurosurgical operation.'

Sheelagh, my wife, had overheard Abby's question, and she subsequently encouraged me to expand on my answer, and to gather together some of my memories and also my thoughts as a neurosurgeon, and indeed to write about them. She reminded me about the conversation, and indeed coaxed me to do so.

The result was that I eventually agreed. I would, hopefully, become an author. It seemed to be a fascinating challenge; it certainly turned out to be a daunting task!

At the onset, I was reminded of two rather amusing stories: the one about the novice strip-tease dancer, who was very concerned that 'too much may be revealed'! The second story concerns the two cows munching away in a field, when a large tanker with the word MILK in large letters painted on the side came along the nearby road. Maisie turned round to Daisy, and said: 'It really makes me feel rather inadequate'!

Considering three possible categories of readers of this book: my family, medical people and intelligent lay people, my personal aim has been to give an example, myself, of becoming a neurosurgeon, and to provide, quite briefly, information on the main scope of neurosurgery, to encourage readers to think – but not to be too presumptuous, and, indeed, also to entertain.

Our lives are an adventure from the moment we are born.

This memoir extends from my early days, to becoming a consultant neurosurgeon in the Department of Clinical Neurosciences in Edinburgh, and Senior Lecturer in Neurosurgery at the University of Edinburgh, then continuing private clinical work for a further five years.

For the benefit of lay (non-medical) readers there is a Glossary of several medical terms used in the text, explaining their meaning in a simple way. This is at the end of the book.

It is my wish that the profits from the sale of the book should be divided and donated to fully recognised and fully accepted medical organisations concerned with researches in the field of (a) Spinal Disorders and (b) Epilepsy.

Acknowledgements

After a longish gestation period, my book has actually been born, and the accoucheuse did a pretty fine job, I think.

However, the advice and help from several people was obviously necessary, and I thank all of them.

Meg Ross, my appointed editor, has always been helpful.

I express my gratitude to Professor Dugald Gardner, pathologist and curator of the Royal College of Surgeons of Edinburgh (RCSE) museum, who carefully scrutinised the text of the book and provided me with several useful, meticulous comments.

Wonderful assistance was obtained from the libraries of the two Edinburgh College libraries. In the RCSE library, Marianne Smith, Andrew McGregor and Steve Kerr were superbly helpful; and in the RCPE library, Ian Milne and Estella Dukin did much to assist me.

A close friend, now unfortunately deceased, Dr Cameron (Cam) Gould, microbiologist, provided useful remarks.

A professional photographer of note, Max McKenzie's work is clearly shown in pages of the book.

A key person involved is my super secretary, Sophie Andrades, a lovely person. She is able to decipher my awful longhand scrawl. I do everything in longhand, no 'machines'.

Lynn Davidson and her staff of the Memoir Club in Durham, have been, from the word 'go' until the completion of the book, patient, understanding and really helpful. It has been a pleasure to work with them.

A special thanks to the illustrious Sir David Carter for his remarkably generous Foreword. Reading it makes me blush!

Several members of my family have also had their 'pennyworth' of comments and advice. I thank them.

Sheelagh, my wife, who indeed initiated my endeavours, has been, at all times, most supportive, encouraging and understanding.

All reasonable efforts have been made to locate the owners of the copyright material. Acknowledgements will be given in reprints if the copyright owner comes forward.

CHAPTER 1

Personal

Early days

I ENTERED LIFE IN OUR HOME in Edinburgh on 28 March 1922, and had a happy, I would say normal, childhood with my parents and David, my younger brother. We were both sent to the excellent Royal High School in Edinburgh.

My old school is indeed an old school, being associated with the Abbey of Holyrood in the twelfth century, 1128, some 879 years ago, and known as the 'Tounis Schule'. James VI in 1591 gave it the royal title: 'Schola Regia Edinburgensis'. It so happens that about this time the boys did not feel that they were having sufficient holidays, and in 1595 they staged a great 'barring out', a strike. Bailie McMoran (the chief magistrate) and town officers forced entry, but a pupil shot and indeed killed the Bailie. Subsequently the School Rule (XVII) includes: 'No gunpowder, fireworks or fire-arms are permitted.'

In my time the school was located on Calton Hill, overlooking the Palace of Holyroodhouse and Princes Street. The playing fields were at Jock's Lodge, some two miles away, adjacent to the preparatory (junior) part of the school. There was another small playing field, within the Palace of Holyroodhouse grounds: school sport therefore on Royal grounds, quite unusual!

I really enjoyed my time at school, finding masters (and in the prep school, mistresses) to be friendly, understanding and obviously skilled in their special subjects. At no time did I come across bullying. There were some transgressions, including smoking – of cinnamon sticks, then of cigarettes – one could buy a single Woodbine cigarette in a shop for one penny. I do not know of drugs being used.

The distinguished classical scholar W. King-Gillies (known by the boys as 'the beak') was the Rector. He was a stern, serious, but lively and formidable gentleman, an excellent teacher and organiser, a disciplinarian. Physical punishment for wrong doers was by the use of a strap (belt). Most masters on occasion used this; there were no complaints by the boys or their parents. Latin was compulsory, and, in the 'A' stream, also Greek; David my brother did Greek.

During assembly in the Great Hall, one morning, a boy sitting on the opposite side to where I was sitting suddenly gave out a loud shriek, followed by what appeared to me to be strange movements of his body and limbs. This was my first experience of epilepsy.

My best subjects at school were history, science and gymnastics. In athletics I participated mainly in the 100 and the 200 yards sprints, and in relays, winning medals. On one occasion I was a member of an Edinburgh schoolboy athletic team competing in Glasgow with Glasgow schoolboys. I believe we won.

Boys at the Royal High soon became aware of the great traditions of the famous school. Former pupils included a number of celebrities in all walks of life including such medical luminaries as the three anatomists, Monro Primus, Secundus and Tertius; the discoverer and the use of chloroform – James Y. Simpson; the introducer of antisepsis – Lord Lister; and the eminent surgeon, Syme. Amongst other former pupils of the school were Sir Walter Scott, Boswell, Fettes, Graham Bell, George Drummond, Robert Fergusson, Allan Ramsay, and also Queen Victoria's son, the Prince of Wales, who became King Edward VII.

Another medical connection with my school in those distant days was the subsequent use of the Royal High School building, the one built in 1777 and abandoned in 1829, to be converted into the surgical part of the Royal Infirmary of Edinburgh, including conversion of the janitor's lodge into wards, becoming apparently, the first hospital in the world specifically for the treatment of patients with serious burns.

In my final year at school, my form master, Mr Norman (Norrie) Dickson, unexpectedly asked each boy in his form what they hoped to do when they left school. I blurted out: 'A doctor, Sir,' and was told that 'If you have that ambition, Harris, you would certainly require to work very much harder!'

Some boys in our form had nicknames; mine was 'Haggis'. (Silly!)

In 1978 I was honoured by being elected President of the Former Pupils' (FP) Club, for the year.

At the end of each school year (session) there is an important day set aside for the presentation of prizes, speeches by the Rector and by the President of the FP Club, and one by the Dux of the school. Then each boy (during my time there were no girl pupils; this occurred much later) leaving school for the very last time, lines up, says goodbye and shakes hands with the Rector, and with a piper playing, passes through the Memorial Doors, to be greeted outside by the President of the FP Club:

the boys 'are entering the adult world'! In my time as FP President, I noticed some boys, sturdy, athletic types, with obvious moist eyes! An emotional event never to be forgotten in their lives.

There are a flood of memories for me at the time. World War II had started, in September 1939.

A German bomber plane, apparently attempting to bomb Rosyth Naval Dockyard and the Forth railway bridge, on 16 October 1939 was shot down and two German airmen were killed. That night, several barrage balloons with trailing wire ropes were placed around Rosyth and the bridge, remaining in place until the end of the war. Anderson corrugated iron air-raid shelters were provided for the garden of each house. I tried to fix electric light in ours but only succeeded in fusing all of the house lights! Deep air-raid shelters were made under Princes Street Gardens. All iron gates and railings were removed (and were never replaced). The iron was necessary to be melted down and made into various items for the war.

Our family holidays were usually spent in Scotland, including North Berwick, Arran, Rothesay, Ayr, Prestwick, Gullane and in some places in 'the Kingdom of Fife'. A relation of my father lived in Lundin Links, in Fife, which was very popular with Edinburgh schoolchildren in the summer; there was golf, swimming, tennis, and a fine Pierrot show; we loved it. A very early memory, I would be aged three or four years, was of being on a train crossing over the Forth railway bridge, with my maternal grandfather. I saw what appeared to me to be tiny people and motor cars down below, rather cute! And we practised the custom of throwing a penny out of the train window, over the bridge, and making a wish. We were indeed going over the bridge, from South to North Queensferry.

One mischievous ploy with other boys at play, was to ask an unsuspecting boy unfamiliar with our nonsense, to ride his bicycle with his arms crossed over on the handlebars – the person always falls off! Please, reader, do not attempt this trick!

Another 'medical memory' as a schoolboy was being taken to a certain Edinburgh shoe shop for new shoes. After trying shoes on, the young customer was asked to place his feet into a gap in a machine, and he actually then saw an outline of the bones of feet and the outline of the new shoes. This was my first experience of X-rays. (Obviously such machines were, later, banned.)

I had personal knowledge of two young cousins who unfortunately developed fatal illnesses. One had Hodgkin's disease – a form of cancer –

and did not survive long. The other, a charming intelligent girl, had rheumatic fever, and later died from 'an infected heart': obviously subacute bacterial endocarditis (SBE). These were awful illnesses, which greatly upset me at my early age; if only something could have been done! Of course in later years both of these diseases usually respond well to modern treatment.

We had a wonderful general practitioner (GP), Dr Matheson, a tall, elegant friendly gentleman wearing a Marlborough suit (black jacket and striped trousers) and a bowler hat. He liked doing house calls and was very popular, especially with children. He came in his gleaming car, accompanied by his dog. Dr Matheson smoked cigars, and the aroma remained in our home after his visit.

Other medical memories include some of my leisure time reading, as a young person. Such books included Thomas Mann's *The Magic Mountain*; Axel Munthe's *Story of San Michele*; A. J. Cronin's *The Citadel*; a biography by the Curies; and one on *The Microbe Hunters*.

With friends, as a schoolboy, I carried out some chemistry 'experiments', but one day caused an explosion in the basement of a friend's home. Fortunately no one was injured, but 'no more chemistry there'!

Another memory – the Palace Cinema, at the East End of Princes Street (at one time there were four cinemas in that famous street), not far from my school in Regent Road, at one time was showing a film – admittance only for those over eighteen years. The title was *Damaged Goods*; it was indeed about a subject not well known by schoolchildren then, venereal diseases (VD).

School golf was very popular, but I never made the team. However I played on the eighteen-hole Braid Hills courses. Number two was three (old) pence a round, and number one, 'expensive', at sixpence a round.

Another golfing incident occurring later in my life: a young man was teaching his equally young – and pretty – fiancée to play the game. 'Take a much fuller swing,' he said. These were the last words he remembered, as his lady accidentally struck her fiancé on the top of his head, causing a compound depressed fracture of the skull, but only minor brain damage. We operated on him in our Department. He made a full recovery, and indeed they had a happy marriage.

I hark back to my quite happy schooldays with the school song ringing in my head: '*Schola Regia Edinensis*'; and remembering the school motto: *Musis Republica Floret*.

Family

Lily, one of my mother's sisters, lived in Glasgow, and a nearby neighbour was the Coutts family, who had a young daughter, Sheelagh. When visiting Glasgow one day I was introduced to Sheelagh, and was immediately attracted to the lovely, petite, charming young lady. She and I enjoyed each other's company very much, and there were many car and train journeys between Edinburgh and Glasgow, and pleasant visits to the Scottish highlands, culminating in June 1949, during a visit to Gleneagles Hotel in Perthshire, when Sheelagh graciously accepted my proposal of marriage. We were married in Glasgow on 7 November 1949, and have been happily married for some fifty-nine years, and have two children. Our daughter Frances is a physiotherapist, married to David, an accountant, who have twins, Shiona and Alasdair; and Harvey, our son, is a lawyer in Glasgow, married to Sandra, a general practitioner, and they have two girls, Abigail and Samantha.

Sheelagh is a lovely lady, astute and very determined, a wonderful wife, mother and grandmother. She was active in several spheres of charitable and voluntary work, including Chairman of the Edinburgh Children's Welfare Group; member of the Edinburgh Guild of Service Adoption Committee; and of the Council of Social Services, being concerned with case work; President of the Edinburgh Inner Wheel Club (linked to the Rotary Club of Edinburgh). She started the University of Edinburgh Riding Club.

Whilst still engaged, I required to go one day to the home of my chief Professor Norman Dott, to obtain some teaching slides for a lecture I was due to give (he kept such slides in his home). I went up to his study, obtained the slides, and had an interesting discussion on neurosurgery with him. But time was passing, it was now dark outside. I mentioned that my fiancée was out in my car. Eventually we went downstairs, hearing voices from the sitting room, and found Sheelagh having tea with Mrs Dott. We joined them. Later in the car I asked Sheelagh how she got on with Mrs Dott. 'Very well,' she said. Also, that Mrs Dott said that being a neurosurgeon's wife could be a bit difficult at times: long hours, seven days a week, many phone calls, little free time. Later that evening I took my fiancée out for a nice dinner in a restaurant. We were indeed going to get married!

One afternoon Sheelagh was driving Harvey, our son, and two of his friends to an Edinburgh golf course, but on the way, another vehicle shot out of a side road, colliding with Sheelagh's car – which became a write-off. She sustained a head injury and was unconscious. Harvey had telephoned me at my office in our Department and the ambulance brought Sheelagh there. She had regained consciousness. I had contacted my colleague, John Gillingham, who kindly looked after Sheelagh. She made an excellent recovery. One of the boys had minor cuts and bruises and a swollen knee. The headline in the *Daily Express* newspaper the following day was 'Surgeon's Wife in Car Crash Drama'.

At one time I was having some difficulty in getting off to sleep at nights, and our GP prescribed Nembutal (a barbiturate, subsequently, in 1986, discontinued). Sheelagh was not happy about my being on this, or any drug, and, without my knowledge, she emptied the capsules, replacing the drug with sugar. The now inert capsules were still effective: a 'placebo effect'. But soon I was told what she had done.

We were very fortunate in having the help of Sheelagh's own Nanny, Miss Marion McNeil, who had looked after Sheelagh since she was aged six months, and had really become one of the Coutts family. She was a delightful, caring person. Nurse, as I called her, was most helpful with our own children and, indeed, made it possible for Sheelagh and me to be away from our home for medical meetings, and for social occasions.

Sitting in the Taj Palace Intercontinental Hotel in New Delhi, India, at the conclusion of a World Congress on Neurosurgery, waiting on transport to the airport, I noticed Sheelagh check the time, saying, *sotto voce*: 'They will be closed now!' I asked who 'they' were, and was told that when I went with her along with the wife of an Indian neurosurgeon we visited a jeweller's shop in the city and Sheelagh saw something that she had really liked. I excused myself and telephoned Sheelagh's friend, who said that she knew the owner of the shop and that she would telephone him and explain the situation. I thanked her. Sure enough, a gentleman arrived in the hotel lobby, and recognised Sheelagh. He joined us and I watched her surprise, as he opened a small box, revealing a pair of lovely ear-rings. She gladly accepted them, my ruby anniversary present for her!

We have been privileged to meet several interesting and important people, concerned with medical, especially neurosurgical, affairs, and also in relation to voluntary and charitable bodies – mainly involving physically and mentally disabled people: The Queen and the Duke of Edinburgh, in Buckingham Palace, and in the Palace of Holyroodhouse, The Queen Mother, Prince Charles, Princess Margaret, Princess Anne, and the

Duchesses of Kent and of Gloucester. There was also the pleasure of meeting three Prime Ministers: Harold Wilson in London, after the Paraplegic Games in Israel, and at different times Edward Heath and Margaret Thatcher: they both visited my ward in the Department of Surgical Neurology, Western General Hospital, Edinburgh.

My father was a firm, but not too serious, friendly, book-loving, very active man, who served as a soldier in World War I, mainly in the Middle East. He was somewhat taciturn about his battle experiences, but we did know that at one time he was very ill with malaria. On demobilisation he joined the family business of wholesale fruit merchants specialising in bananas. These arrived in Scotland hard and dark green in colour, and after a period of ripening in the firm's hot-houses, they were sold. My father was a keen golfer, playing regularly in one of the three golf clubs of which he was a member. Other special interests included the Freemasons, apparently reaching a senior position, and the British Legion, including an annual visit to London for the Armistice Service.

My mother, a lovely elegant happy lady, had many close friends, and was involved in some charitable-social activities. She and my father were surely 'made for each other', and were wonderful parents for David and myself. In a quiet but positive way they wisely guided me in my schooldays, and later on when I was a medical student. I am extremely grateful to them. Although I was keen to practise medicine, my father introduced me to his legal friends and also to journalists in the *Scotsman* newspaper office, 'just in case', but neither law nor journalism were for me, I finally decided.

In the early hours one morning, Frances, our daughter, then a physiotherapy student, was returning with friends from a formal ball in evening dress, when they were surprised to come across a large horse, by itself, ambling along Fountainbridge, an Edinburgh street. Frances was good with horses, and she led the animal back some distance to the Co-operative Society Stables. Horses were then used to pull milk floats. Somehow the press heard about the incident, and in the newspapers there was a headline: 'After the Ball – The Horse Shoe Shuffle'!

My paternal grandfather had a fish business in Fife; his wife, my paternal grandmother, was a schoolteacher. I do not remember either of them.

My maternal grandfather was a master craftsman, literally making lovely shoes. As a schoolboy I was fascinated watching him at work. Outwith work his main interests were his nine grandchildren. We assembled in his home on Sundays. He had 'green fingers', growing fine flowers, and tasty vegetables.

Sheelagh's father was a popular, well known person in Glasgow, a gentleman of many parts, involved in a number of philanthropic activities and with a wide circle of close friends, in business, the professions and in politics. He was a clothing manufacturer in Glasgow, Manchester and Leeds. I understand that he played an important part in identifying the nefarious activities of Captain Archibald Ramsay, the Member of Parliament for Peebles in Scotland. Ramsay supported Hitlerism, including persecution of Jewish people. He was a traitor, preferring the enemy as an ally rather than an enemy in World War II. He was imprisoned. My father-in-law received a nice personal letter of thanks from Mr (as he was then) Winston Churchill.

Sheelagh's mother, a small lovely dynamic person, the youngest of several children, was a delightful lady, always keen to help people in a most practical way; she was a fine cook and hostess.

During World War II Sheelagh's parents were most pleased to care for a young child, aged two and a half years, a refugee from Nazi Germany. Marion, a blue-eyed blonde girl, whose parents were probably in a concentration camp – alive or dead – became one of the Coutts family. We became aware of the horrific slaughter occurring in the concentration camps; and knew about the 'Kindertransport', the name given to the rescue mission that took place nine months prior to the outbreak of World War II. The UK took in nearly ten thousand predominantly Jewish children from Nazi Germany and adjacent countries, who were placed in foster homes, hostels and farms.

Paul, one of my father's brothers, was an interesting person, a newspaper journalist, a writer of books, and a keen spiritualist. He edited the *Psychic News* for some time. He had several important friends, including Air Marshal Lord Dowding (Battle of Britain), and the writer Hannen Swaffer. I attended a couple of séances, but I remain sceptical.

Another literary family member is Dr David Rubin, my cousin, a psychiatrist and author, now living in Costa Rica. He wrote the best seller *Everything You Always Wanted to Know About Sex, But Were Afraid To Ask* which was made into a popular film starring Woody Allen.

A cousin of Sheelagh, Julius Green, a dentist, and a great raconteur, was an Army Dental Officer in World War II. He was captured by the Germans, but as a dentist was made use of, travelling to various prisoner of war (POW) camps. Whilst doing so he was able to obtain some useful information of some German war activities, and he sent information back to his family in Dublin, in code. Initially they could not understand some of the contents of the letters, but quickly realised why, and passed them on to the Service authorities. Julius (Julie) finished up in Colditz prison, Oflag IVC. A fellow prisoner was the famous Wing Commander Douglas Bader. Julie wrote a book about his exploits: *From Colditz in Code* (1989), which was also serialised in a British national newspaper.

Medical school 1939–44

> It is said in the Talmud: 'Find yourself a teacher.'

Sir Godfrey Housfield, inventor of computerised tomography (CT scanning), was awarded the Nobel Prize. He was a non-graduate. His advice to the young: 'Don't worry if you cannot pass exams, so long as you feel you have understood the subject.'

With the necessary qualifications to be admitted to enter a Medical School, I opted for the School of Medicine of the Scottish Royal Colleges, which had an excellent reputation. I was keen to study in my home city of Edinburgh. My interview with the Dean, Dr John Orr, who had received details of my scholastic and personal attainments and interests, was pleasant and searching. At the conclusion I was informed that I would be accepted to undertake the five-year medical course. I was delighted.

Dr Orr proved to be an excellent medical Dean, was a good administrator, and was well versed in several medical spheres, having had experience as a general practitioner (GP), as a hospital clinician and as a demonstrator in anatomy, and having taught medicine, materia medica, and midwifery. The medical historian Douglas Guthrie said that 'Dr John Orr was most popular, and was beloved and respected by successive generations of students during his long term as Dean.' I always remember the excellent Secretary of the Medical School, Miss Georgina M. Lamb, a most helpful and friendly lady, with whom students often spoke for wise advice.

Medical education in Edinburgh began in 1505 with the incorporation of barber surgeons. In time, some barber surgeons only did surgery, no barbering, but the title of 'Mr', and not 'Dr' was retained. This is presumably the reason why, up to the present time in Britain, surgeons in most surgical specialties are known as 'Mr', and not 'Dr': that is, once they have successively passed the Fellowship examination of one of the British Royal Colleges of Surgeons.

Prior to the founding of the Edinburgh University Faculty of Medicine, the School of Medicine of the Scottish Royal Colleges was incorporated by Charter in 1895. The School had a major influence on the course of medical education in Edinburgh, indeed achieving world-wide recognition, and was an important recruiting ground from which many University professors were chosen. The School of Medicine supplied thirty-five professors to the Medical Faculty of Edinburgh University, and with the inclusion of other Universities, a total of sixty-one professors (Guthrie 1965). There was great emphasis on anatomy; indeed it was stated in the Charter of the School of Medicine 'That we may have enis in the year ane condampint man efter he be died, to make an anatomea of quarterow we may hef experience ill ane to instruct uthers and we sall de suffrage for the soule.'

The Medical School was internationally famous, with many celebrated teachers, including the three Monros, anatomists, Primus, Secondus and Tertius; John Bell; Charles Bell; John Lizars; Robert Knox, a brilliant anatomist physiologist and pathologist, a wonderful orator and lecturer, with some five hundred students attending his classes (there was the unfortunate association with Burke and Hare); Lister; Littlejohn; Liston; Argyll Robertson; and James Y. Simpson. Also Sir David Wilkie, and Sir John Fraser.

Some of my medical teachers gave didactic lectures and were also involved in hospital clinics; others mainly did bedside teaching. They included such luminaries as Professor Sir Derrick Dunlop (physician); Professor Sir John Fraser (surgeon); Mr J. Mason Brown (paediatric surgeon); Dr Charles Whittaker (anatomist); Professor Sir Stanley Davidson (physician); Dr Douglas Guthrie (otolaryngology, and medical historian); Dr Clifford Kennedy (obstetrics and gynaecology); Dr R. F. Illingworth (chemistry); Mr C. N. Kemp (physics); Professor D. J. A. Kerr (forensic medicine); Mr John ('Jock') Struthers (surgery); Professor Sir Walter Mercer (surgery); Professor Alexander Kennedy (psychological medicine); and Dr Henry Dryere (physiology).

In biology, we were required to dissect an earthworm, a skate (a fish), and a frog.

Professor Sir John Fraser Bt., Regius Professor of Clinical Surgery, was a brilliant surgeon and teacher, attracting large numbers of students to his lectures and clinics and to his operating theatre in the Royal Infirmary of Edinburgh (RIE). His forebears were farmers. His surgical mentor was the distinguished surgeon Sir Harold Stiles, whom he succeeded. Sir John made full use of the frosted window in his operating theatre, rapidly drawing in coloured chalks appropriate sketches to accompany his words. I can picture him now, wearing his white coat with short sleeves, always business-like, but friendly and smiling, always 'in his element', loving his job. He was a master showman. His surgical background was extensive, including paediatric surgery – in particular bone and joint tuberculosis. But he was a supreme general surgeon. I had the good fortune to be a student in his clinic, and was allowed to assist him during some of his operations. I remember scrubbing up alongside him, and one morning he said: 'Harris, the water is cold [saving fuel in war-time], but is just as clean as warm water!' In these war times there were many shortages; even used swabs were washed and re-sterilised, and gloves were checked for holes, which were then repaired and the gloves re-used time and time again.

Dr Charles Whittaker, a Yorkshireman, was an inspiring teacher of anatomy, explaining and demonstrating on cadavers and a skeleton the wonders of the human body. His rapid blackboard drawings in coloured chalks accompanied his fine lectures. He was indeed an artist, a painter, mainly of attractive cubist works, and was Professor of Anatomy to the Royal Scottish Academy in Edinburgh. In my time we did five terms of anatomy, with dissection of the whole of the human body. Demonstrators were available. I was fortunate in being appointed a student demonstrator, both in the School of Medicine and in the University of Edinburgh Medical School. In the Royal College of Surgeons Medical School a summer course in anatomy took place; I enjoyed teaching in it. The majority of the medical students were from Oxford University.

Our psychiatry (psychological medicine) teacher was the inspiring learned doctor Professor Alexander Kennedy. His teachings were pertinent and fascinating; and I remember much of them, including his demonstrations of therapeutic hypnosis and teaching his students to carry out hypnosis. Apparently during World War II he jumped with paratroopers to obtain first hand experiences of possible psychological reactions that can occur in such soldiers. I also heard that he was an author and a playwright.

The physician Professor Sir Derrick Dunlop was a suave, tall, elegant, erudite gentleman, well versed in the classics. His lectures and orations were wonderful and memorable, as were his hospital ward rounds in the RIE. During his lectures, young lady medical students would gaze intently at 'the Ivor Novello of the Edinburgh Medical School'. A favourite topic was diet and dieting, about which he was an expert; we were reminded that 'we dig our own graves with our teeth'!

It is to be appreciated that during my time as a medical student World War II was raging, affecting all our lives, in several ways, in Britain. Indeed early in the War a German invasion of Britain was felt to be almost imminent. There was blackout, food rationing, and rationing of fuel and of clothes. Many children from urban centres were evacuated to countryside havens, some being sent overseas by ships, mainly to North America. Everyone was required to carry their gas mask at all times, ready for use.

The teaching and training of medical students continued; sometimes practical war-time problems required to be overcome. There was a shortage of medical doctors 'for home use', and some senior medical students were given hospital jobs as 'student house physicians and surgeons', but were not allowed to prescribe dangerous drugs, nor to sign death certificates. I had such a job, staying in and working in the Southern General Hospital in Edinburgh. This was an unexpected benefit from the horrific war. It so happened that I developed a nasty, acute rash of my hands, requiring various therapies, and was advised that 'whatever you decide to do once you are qualified as a doctor, do not become a surgeon.' I am afraid that this was one piece of medical advice that I ignored!

The functions of a Medical School are to teach to pursue the truth, to have teachers and facilities of excellence, and to carry out examinations of the students and to encourage participation in discussions and controversies. We had excellent teachers. There were several student organisations to cater for our varied interests. I assisted with publication of the Medical School journal and I particularly enjoyed the Dialectic Group where we had excellent philosophical, ethical and moral discussions. The Edinburgh University Students' Union was a popular rendezvous. The Edinburgh Medical Schools have always attracted students from near and far, including the UK countries, USA, Canada, the Middle East, India, Pakistan, Africa and Australia. This gave added interest and lustre for all of us. We had an intensive five-year course in the Medical School. The subjects included biology, physics, botany, chemistry, anatomy, physiology, pathology, bacteriology, therapeutics, medicine, public health, pharmacology, surgery, obstetrics and gynaecology, forensic medicine, psychiatry, and 'the specials': ophthalmology, otolaryngology, dermatology, and venereal diseases. In addition to didactic lectures, there were seminars and hospital clinics. All were important and excellent. Indeed the internationally famous American physician Sir William Osler, the first Professor of Medicine in the John Hopkins University in Baltimore, USA was so impressed with the Edinburgh clinical teaching that he copied the style in his own Department.

During the course of studies DP (Duly Performed) tests were mandatory, students gaining certificates. There were strict professional examinations, culminating in 'the finals'. Much learning indeed! Successful students gained the Triple Qualifications of the Scottish Royal Colleges.

We became familiar with the Medical School region of Edinburgh, Teviot Place, Lauriston Place, Forrest Road, the Royal Infirmary, the Students' Union, and the Royal College of Surgeons. Hospitals used for teaching included the RIE, the Western General Hospital (WGH), the Northern General Hospital (NGH), the Royal Hospital for Sick Children (RHSC: 'Sick Kids'), the Royal Edinburgh Hospital (REH), and the Fever Hospital (FH). As a medical student I was not pleased with the names of two of the Edinburgh hospitals: The Princess Margaret Rose Hospital for Crippled Children was mainly for orthopaedic patients, with tuberculosis or poliomyelitis, but the awful word, 'crippled'! Then, Longmore Hospital for Incurables was for pre-terminal or terminal patients with some form of cancer, but again an awful word, 'incurables'!

Before the inception of the NHS in Britain in 1948, hospitals such as the RIE were 'voluntary hospitals', relying on private funding from donations: the walls of the main corridors of that hospital were covered with the names and bequests of donors. During one week in the year the medical and dental students organised a number of money raising events for the hospitals, including street and door to door collections and a procession of gloriously decorated lorry floats with bands and dressed up students, parading along the main streets of Edinburgh. There were also variety shows in the New Victoria Cinema: and an amusing, somewhat 'daring' magazine, called *Euragonna*!

The senior (non-professional) medical staff of the RIE, a voluntary hospital, were unpaid. The senior consultant ('the Chief') controlled all of the beds in his female and male wards. The junior consultant ('assistant' surgeon or physician) was allowed, with the permission of the Chief, use of some of the beds. The income of senior medical staff came mainly from private practice carried out in private nursing homes and from teaching, and also by acting as examiners of undergraduate and postgraduate students. The chief was in office for only fifteen years.

In my second year, a fellow student, whose father was a consultant surgeon in a London teaching hospital and also had a practice in the famous Harley Street, and I crept into the viewing gallery (junior students were not meant to do this) of one of the RIE operating theatres to witness our first operation. No sooner had the surgeon made his first incision when my colleague fainted and required assistance to get him out of the theatre. He quickly recovered, and I returned to watch the operation.

One day, during my third year, a fellow student, Tony Donaldson, a close friend, asked if I would like to meet one of his friends, the Resident

House Officer in Ward 20 of the RIE. I accepted, and enjoyed the visit. Little did I realise the importance of this visit for me, as that ward was the Department of Surgical Neurology, and the Chief was the famous Norman Dott. I subsequently returned to that Department on a number of occasions, doing what is termed 'junioring' (in England called 'clerking'), which involved doing some routine urine, blood and faecal tests; to take medical notes, and generally be helpful. Subsequently I was invited at times to be an assistant to the Chief in the operating theatre. One day Professor Dott took me aside, and said that he had noted my interest in the work of the Department, and had found out about my special interests in anatomy and in surgery. He said that I appeared to get on very well both with patients and staff. He then invited me, if I wished, to come on as his Surgical Resident once I was qualified as a doctor. I readily accepted this quite unexpected offer; it was wonderful.

As students, we had a lecture and demonstrations by the formidable but very nice Miss Mann, Head of what was then called the 'Massage Department' (that term could obviously not be used nowadays!). Her young lady students, short skirted, were received with student cheers and applause as they demonstrated therapies of their profession!

We were required to watch a number of autopsies as part of our training, and I well remember one occasion when the subject was a gentleman who had died from cancer of the lung, which had metastasised (spread) to the brain and elsewhere. He had been a heavy smoker of cigarettes. The unusual aspect was that the pathologist was actually himself smoking cigarettes during the autopsy!

The terrible dangers of smoking have been clearly, scientifically shown and published. I myself smoked a pipe or small cigars (cheroots) as a medical student at times. In later life I developed cancer of the larynx, necessitating an operation, followed by a full course of radiotherapy. It was a quite horrible experience but the treatment was fortunately, to date, successful.

I wish to mention two other 'smoking' stories: some years ago, when I spent time in the famous Montreal Neurological Institute, headed by the distinguished neurosurgeon Dr Wilder Penfield, with Sheelagh accompanying me on this trip, we were recommended to visit the World Fair which was on in Montreal, and when there not to miss seeing the lovely Chinese pavilion. We joined the queue to enter it, and noticed that each visitor was handed a small gift package. On opening it we found that it was a packet of cigarettes, with Chinese and English names on the packet stating: 'Long Life Cigarettes'! But the pavilion was wonderful. I would now refer to a

1. Sheelagh and I

2. *My parents*

3. Sheelagh's parents

4. *My father and I*

5. *Dr W. King Gillies, Rector of the Royal High School*. Courtesy of Royal High School

6. *Our wedding on 7 November 1949*

7. *Our wedding. Ann Rowe, cousin, best maid; David, my brother, best man*

8. The family (from left to right): Front: Samantha, Abigail, Alasdair, Shiona. Middle: Sandra, myself, Sheelagh, Frances. Back: Harvey, David

popular British variety artiste who had for some reason apparently changed his name to 'NOSMO KING'. His name would certainly be noted everywhere, but in any case I agree, there should indeed be 'no smoking'!

As a medical student, and subsequently, I have been amused and querulous about the word 'stethoscope'. According to my *Oxford Dictionary*, '*stetho*' pertains to the chest, or breasts, and '*scope*' is to look at, examine, make observations, enabling the eye to view or examine people. '*Phone*' is 'sound'. I was however unable to convince my medical teachers to change 'stethoscope' to 'stethophone'!

More seriously, I have felt that all medical students should be encouraged to spend several hours of one day as a 'wheelchair' individual, to find out at first hand, some of the practical problems for such disabled people who rely on their wheelchair for their everyday activities.

Fire-watching, in relation to the dropping of incendiary bombs, was important during World War II. Buckets of sand and of water and hand pumps were provided. As students we were on a rota, for different locations. Mine were the Royal College of Surgeons; the Plaza Ballroom (it was eerie at night, walking on the bouncy sprung wooden floor, which caused odd loud squeaking noises); and St Trinian's Girls' School in Edinburgh. The school was old, with turrets and many rooms. The girls' sleeping quarters still had notices up saying: 'For mistress please ring the bell'! Some while later, USA soldiers were billeted there, and were quite amused by such notices.

As medical students we were required to administer a number of general anaesthetics, usually open, with a mask, nitrous oxide, chloroform or ether. I cannot recall any real problems arising. Another mandatory requirement was to deliver a number of babies, both 'routine deliveries', and a small number of 'abnormal deliveries'. Unfortunately the pregnant ladies all appeared to reside high up in Edinburgh tenements, and one was hauled out of bed usually in the small hours, on a rainy, blackout night to climb the many stairs. But the mothers were lovely and friendly and congratulated the 'doctor'! A furniture drawer acted as cradle for the new born baby.

Relaxation for medical students in the limited time available away from lectures and clinics and swotting for exams included activities in the University Union; cinemas (entry for a few pence, up to a shilling); bars (including those in the famous Rose Street, which runs parallel to and just north of Princes Street); dancing; cycling; the theatre (cheap high up in 'the gods'); occasionally managing a little golf on the Braid Hills.

My five years of endeavours proved to be successful. I was very pleased to have passed the Finals, and was now a qualified doctor. It called for a celebration!

Resident House Surgeon 1944–45

My first official appointment as a doctor was as Resident House Surgeon to Professor Norman Dott, the Chief in the Department of Surgical Neurology (DSN) in Ward 20, RIE, and Director of the Brain Injuries Unit (BIU), Bangour General Hospital (BGH) (about fifteen miles from Edinburgh). The latter hospital, an EMS (Emergency Medical Service), was used because the Government was concerned about possible wartime German bombing of Edinburgh. The staff of DSN included Mr George Alexander (Assistant Neurosurgeon, who later became Chief of the Neurosurgical Department in Bristol); Dr W. Wilson, Senior Registrar; Dr Kate Herman, medical neurologist; Dr Charles Beevors, crystallographer, in charge of electro-encephalography (EEG); Dr O. Zangwill, clinical psychologist (who later had the Chair in his specialty in Cambridge University); Miss E. Butters, speech therapist; Miss Robertson, Mrs Dott's sister (a fine secretary); and two other important people – Sister Cunningham, Ward Sister, and Sister Ross, Theatre Sister.

The RIE was the main Edinburgh teaching hospital. The general medical and surgical wards were so called (Florence) Nightingale wards, with beds down each side of the long rooms; there were also one or two small bedded wards, a teaching room, a doctors' room and Sister's sitting room. Indeed each of the several 'general wards' were really separate units, with their own staff and usually their own particular special surgical or medical interests and involvements, depending on the special interests of the Chief and his assistant. Two other important people in the RIE were Mr Tom Hurst, Secretary and Treasurer (on his desk, the notice 'The Buck Stops Here'), and, with his tremendous interest and involvement in anti-smoking, being a senior person in the important organisation ASH, Dr S. Francis, the excellent, most approachable and helpful Medical Superintendent.

The middle floor of the RIE surgical block had a rubber (specially donated) floor; the main entrance to the hospital was on this floor, as were the Secretary's and Treasurer's offices; it led into the Residency, for house surgeons and physicians. The Residency was spartan including the drab bedrooms and shower and toilet facilities. There were several unusual customs pertaining to the Residency. It was all male (there were no female residents in my time). There was a system of fines, to help towards Sunday lunch and the occasional special lunches, for example when a new Chief was appointed. Talking 'shop' resulted in a financial penalty, as did wearing a white coat in the mess. Misdemeanours such as not receiving an accurate weekly report by the resident who had been appointed 'Peeping Tom' on the amorous activities of residents and nurses; or throwing 'an edible missile' during Sunday lunch, were also punished. The oldest member was 'father', the youngest was 'babe', and there were special privileges or penalties for each. Each resident was required to carve his name on the wooden tables. I will not say much about some of the high jinks that took place at the end of the duration of the residents' appointments: smoking out the Medical Superintendent; locking a senior nurse for a short time in a bathroom; painting one face of the hospital clock bright red; also, something to do with greased piglets; and a rude awakening of certain people with a number of hens. It should be remembered that residents only received a token payment (hardly a salary); and were required to pay for such items as having their white coats laundered. All of these quaint customs were discontinued when the NHS came in 1948.

My six months as Resident House Surgeon were full of interest and of challenges. Some of our head injury patients came via the Surgical Out-Patient Department of the RIE; especially on Friday and Saturday nights many were drunk. At that time the favourite drinks were cheap Australian wine, methylated spirits or Brasso (a cleaning fluid containing spirits for polishing certain metals), or even a 'cocktail' of coal gas bubbled through milk. There were no 'drugs' such as were later in vogue.

In Ward 20, RIE, there was a modern operating theatre, half dome-shaped to direct the lighting; it was air conditioned with a viewing gallery which was soundproofed, with one way glass – in the theatre you could not see or hear anyone in the gallery, but there was a microphone link with the theatre.

I wish to make special mention of senior nursing staff in hospitals. They are very important people, and with knowledge and understanding of medical matters in hospital. I am certain that many other neophyte doctors find out, in a quiet but useful way, the help they can offer to doctors who have just become responsible for patient care. In the Brain Injuries Unit at Bangour General Hospital, the ward sisters were Marshall, Martin and Hilton.

In Ward 20, RIE, Professor Dott often used stereoscopic X-rays. He was a most caring, personal, doctor, even doing one a.m. telephone ward rounds from his home and asking very pertinent questions! He was a neat, meticulous surgeon, not very quick, but he would often begin a major operation and continue until the dressings were applied by him. Harvey Cushing did the same. I heard him say that 'the weekend was a nice quiet time to operate'.

We were probably one of the first Departments to have the privilege of using the new, wonder drug, penicillin. To begin with it was amber in colour and was thick and almost syrupy when given intrathecally, to a patient with acute meningitis. It was very irritating for the patient – but the effects were excellent and indeed miraculous! Subsequently it was possible to introduce it intravenously, and in Edinburgh, the laboratory produced something special, the Eudrip (Edinburgh University drip).

I will mention one rather amusing outpatient encounter: The gentleman had lumbar backache and sciatica. I clinically examined him when he was standing up, then lying down on his back; then I asked him to turn over onto his front. He knew what I would see, but neither he nor I said anything about what was revealed. Tattooed on his lower back were the words 'I see you' and on each buttock a seeing eye was tattooed! Strange!

Professor Dott took his staff to the circus near the end of each year. We all enjoyed the event, which included what we call in Scotland, high tea.

The Christmas party in the BIU was well attended, and included a gentleman wearing a golf jerkin and baggy flannel trousers, and using two elbow crutches. The new hospital chaplain shook hands and spoke to those present, including that 'patient'. He asked him how he was, 'Not too bad,' and how long he had been in this hospital, 'Oh, about two years!' But Sister whispered that that 'patient' was Professor Dott, convalescing at home from hip surgery, but taken into the ward to join the party!

In the BIU there were two blocks, numbers 9 and 32, each with a number of wards. One ward had only German POW patients. Head injury and spinal injury casualties from the theatres of war were received, many with horrific wounds causing major brain or spinal cord lesions. In 1940, some military casualties had arrived by air to Edinburgh airport within a day from Dunkirk. This would subsequently prove to be what I mainly required to deal with during most of my time as a medical officer in the Royal Army Medical Corps (RAMC), in the Military Hospital for Head Injuries in Oxford.

My six months as a RSO were most valuable to me as a preparation for further, more demanding medical work.

The Royal Army Medical Corps (RAMC) 1945–48

I served in the RAMC from 1945 to 1948, and had routine, non-combatant (for all medical doctors) military training, near Aldershot in England. We also spent time in the Army School of Hygiene, where to my surprise at my first lunch I found a dead beetle, legs upwards, in my mince! I took this to be a cook's joke.

After postings to several Army units in England I was sent to the famous Military Hospital for Head Injuries in Oxford, initially located at Wheatley, later transferred to the Churchill Hospital. Some of us were being trained to form part of a Mobile Neurosurgical Unit to go to Burma, but the war ended for Britain.

The hospital was well staffed, and was under the leadership of two outstanding doctors: Brigadier Sir Hugh Cairns, neurosurgeon, and Air Vice Marshal Sir Charles Symonds, neurologist. A number of young neurosurgical and neurological officers were returning from overseas duties, and several of them later became consultant hospital doctors in their specialty in various British medical centres. I will mention one such doctor in particular: Major James Baird, a good friend, a fine physician and soldier, who later indeed became Lt. General Sir James Baird, in command of the RAMC.

One of my postings was to Southampton Common, near the large Netley Military Hospital. Why there? It soon became obvious. A medical and nursing organisation was set up to screen a large number of women and children who had been in POW camps not far from Hiroshima in Japan, where the first atomic bomb had been exploded in August 1945. Our reports were sent to the authorities regarding any radiation or indeed other systemic or psychological effects.

Some of the service people admitted to the Military Hospital for Head Injuries had sustained terrible physical trauma to brain, spinal cord or nerves; there were also facio-maxillary injuries. Many were neurologically disabled: limbs, speech, epilepsy, paraplegia; several also had serious problems with memory and other intellectual functions. But morale was good. Many lessons had been learnt regarding the awful battle wounds, as well as some non-battle involvement traumas, and as in some other wars over the ages there were some good spin-offs. I refer to the introduction and use of penicillin (discovered by Fleming and developed by Florey), which apparently for the very first time ever was being used by the British Army in the Middle East and in the African battle zones; also the introduction of the valuable Mobile Neurosurgical Units; and, thirdly, the excellent organisation for blood transfusions.

Reparative neurosurgery and facio-maxillary surgery were carried out. Careful documentation was instituted. Essential neurological and psychological therapies were instituted. Post-traumatic epilepsy was studied and treated. There was appropriate rehabilitation and resettlement of many of the injured service patients.

When off duty, I was given permission to visit the Radcliffe Infirmary in Oxford, in particular the neurosurgery, neuropathology and neuro-radiological departments.

One day in the Military Hospital, at about two a.m., I 'lost' my theatre sister. A lady member of the staff had developed acute appendicitis and peritonitis. She was acutely ill and I operated on her as an emergency. The inflamed appendix had ruptured and there was a quite disgusting smell in the operating theatre, which was very warm and without air-conditioning. The theatre sister was overcome by smell and the heat, and, gently, slipped under the operating table in a faint. I had lost her. She was lifted out and soon recovered, and a theatre nurse allowed me to complete the operation.

The Army was an entirely new experience for me, with the discipline, the friendships and the varied and interesting responsibilities.

My time for demobilisation neared, and one day I was approached and invited to consider taking up a short term commission and be promoted to Major from Captain, but although I had enjoyed my time in the RAMC, I declined. I was young, and strongly wished to begin to study and train, hopefully to become in time a consultant surgeon.

Modern neurosurgery

It is of interest and importance to have some knowledge of the early days of 'modern neurosurgery'.

To begin with, there were general surgeons, some of whom had a particular interest in neurosurgery. Then a small number devoted their practice to neurosurgery; a good example was the situation in the National Hospital for Nervous Diseases, Queen Square, in London, where in 1886 *Sir Victor Horsley* became a full time neurosurgeon. He was a neurophysiologist and operated on animals in the Brown Institute in London, before going to Queen Square. But the neurologists held the fort. At Queen Square, Horsley had no beds of his own, no laboratory, and no surgical service. He was 'a passive surgical technician', only operating by the invitation of the neurologists. (Later, I will mention the Horsley-Clarke stereotactic frame and its use in neurosurgery.) He died in 1916. He had not established an eponymous school of neurosurgery.

Another early pioneer was William Macewen of Glasgow, famous for his work on brain abscesses (1893), but he also did not establish a school of neurosurgery. He had refused the post of chief surgeon at John Hopkins Hospital in Baltimore, USA in 1889. That post was given to the young, brilliant surgeon William Halstead, who subsequently developed a wonderful school of surgery, and included Walter Dandy, Harvey Cushing and Wilder Penfield as his pupils.

Harvey Cushing is known as 'the Father of modern neurosurgery'. He trained under the famous physician William Osler, and the brilliant surgeon William Halstead – who, with Cushing, established the idea of a clinical scientist. Dandy had developed the wonderful radiological technique of air ventriculography, to outline the ventricles (cavities) of the brain; thus, without the need for surgical invasion of the brain, demonstrating tumours and certain other intracranial lesions. Initially, operations by Cushing (craniotomies) for brain tumours were often negative, and there was a feud between Cushing and Dandy, but later, air ventriculography was accepted by Cushing.

As a young doctor, Cushing had travelled to Europe, visiting and studying in medical and surgical centres, in particular in Cambridge under the famous neurophysiologist Sir Charles Sherrington, and in Switzerland the distinguished surgeon Kocher.

It has been said that Cushing was somewhat moody, could be very trying, and was a good talker, but a poor listener. However, he had an extensive neurosurgical practice, doing very many operations, introducing new techniques and writing detailed notes, with many publications. He developed an extensive training programme for surgeons who had already undergone training in general surgery. John Fulton, Cushing's biographer, described him as 'a scientist and pathfinder, artist, writer, and bibliophile, yet, above all, a good doctor'.

Professor Norman McOmish Dott (1897–1973) was my main neuro-surgical mentor. He was of Huguenot origin. The family were immigrants, escaping the persecution of Protestants. He said that so many British people were also, previously, immigrants. The breadwinner in the family was a shoemaker who settled in Cupar, Fife. His grandfather was an art dealer.

The early history of Dott becoming a medical student is very important. After leaving school (Heriot's, in Edinburgh) he began to train as an engineer, but he had an accident when coming down Lothian Road in Edinburgh on his motor-cycle. He was taken to the RIE where he was found to have serious trauma to his left hip and leg. Treatment was satisfactory, but he was left with a painful leg and a permanent limp. He was fascinated by the hospital activities and indeed decided to become a medical student and eventually a surgeon. Later, he obtained the FRCSE, and worked under the physiologist Sir Edward Sharpey-Schafer, in particular carrying out studies on the pituitary gland (which is located in the head). The work was awarded by a Rockefeller Fellowship with Dr Harvey Cushing in the Peter Bent Brigham Hospital in Boston (the PBBH). He had a year there, and was greatly impressed by Cushing, a hard working neurosurgeon with many original ideas. Cushing strongly advised him to develop neurosurgery in Edinburgh. Dott initially did paediatric general surgery, but later started a career in neurosurgery. There was no such specialty in Edinburgh, so he operated in private nursing homes, but fortunately the distinguished Professor Sir David Wilkie gave him some of his beds in the RIE. Then, with monies from the Rockefeller Foundation and from a Scottish industrialist, Sir Alexander Grant, a neurosurgical department was established in Ward 20, RIE. In 1947 he was appointed to the Forbes Chair of Neurosurgery in Edinburgh. He invented new instruments and devised some new operations – including the first ever treatment of a cerebral aneurysm, on the middle cerebral artery, by wrapping it with crushed muscle; and was the first person to reveal a cerebral arteriovenous lesion (a vascular abnormality) by contrast angiography. He was co-founder of the SBNS.

At the end of 1930 a new neurosurgeon was required and was advertised for at the National Hospital for Nervous Diseases, Queen Square, London, to support Horsley; Dott, Jefferson and Cairns were being considered, but Dott did not have an English Surgical Fellowship (FRCSEng), therefore he was not interviewed. Several years later, I had a similar experience when I was a Senior Registrar in the Department of Surgical Neurology in Edinburgh. I had considered applying for a Consultant Neurosurgeon post in a London hospital, but the advertisements in the medical journals clearly stated: Fellowship of the Royal College of Surgeons of England is necessary. I was a Fellow of the Royal College of Surgeons of Edinburgh, and therefore was excluded from applying. Both Jefferson and Cairns stated that they wanted to be able to make their own diagnoses on patients, to determine their management, and to operate 'with extreme care'. At that hospital the physicians (medical neurologists) made the diagnosis and decided management if surgery was indicated – to be done by a general surgeon with an interest in neurosurgery. The appointment was given to Mr Julian Taylor.

The neurosurgical facilities at Bangour had become quite unsuitable. A new, custom built department of neurosurgery was required. With government funding of some £500,000 this indeed became a wonderful reality, as part of the Western General Hospital in Edinburgh. It was a glorious concept, for a comprehensive neurosurgical department. There were three floors, each with twenty beds; two modern operating theatres with special ventilation and lighting and screening for electro-neurophysiological studies; an excellent radiology department; facilities for frozen section pathology studies; ophthalmology and electro-encephalography rooms; physiotherapy; hydrotherapy; occupational therapy; speech therapy; a social worker; clinical neuropsychology, and rooms for teaching, doctors, secretaries and senior nursing staff. DSN/WGH was opened triumphantly in 1960, when the patients were ambulanced in from Bangour Hospital. Each consultant neurosurgeon (Dott, Gillingham and myself) had a floor of twenty beds, and each had two ward sisters, a physiotherapist and an occupational therapist. Each of us had our own out-patient days, waiting lists, and operating days (one or two theatres), also pursuing our own particular interests in neurosurgery. We all cared for head injury patients and other acute emergency neurosurgical conditions. A special celebration for the opening was a superb neurosurgical meeting of the French Society of Neurosurgery and the SBNS, and Sheelagh and I arranged the medical and social aspects.

One day, Professor Dott wrote to Jefferson asking him to treat his awful intractable left leg pain by carrying out an anterolateral cordotomy (under local anaesthetic, to obtain the patient's assistance for the level and extent of loss of pain sensation). The exposed spinal cord is gently rotated, to reveal the anterolateral region (on the opposite side of the body where pain was being experienced, because the pain tracts cross over) and a cut of a few millimetres is made in the spinal cord. But Jefferson's response, initially, was 'no' because he was not absolutely certain that the pain would be permanently abolished. But Dott was (as usual) very determined, and Sir Geoffrey gave in. He operated in Manchester, with Cairns assisting. They were a remarkable trio, pioneers of British neurosurgery. The pain was however only relieved for a short time, and recurred. Next, therefore, an arthodosis (surgical fixation of a joint) of the left hip was carried out also in Manchester, by Sir Harry Platt. Then Dott got Sir Walter Mercer, in the

RIE, to shorten his good (right) leg to make the legs of equal length. But he tripped over his large dog and refractured the right leg leading to more treatment and convalescence.

I remember when we, as a neurosurgical team, went to Oslo, Norway, to Professor Kristian Kristianson's neurosurgical department. The reason was that a child had bled intracranially from a vascular malformation of the brain. The lesion was large and was deeply situated, making neurosurgery somewhat hazardous. A new technique was available in Oslo, to selectively cool the brain by passing the patient's blood supply to the brain through a special cooling apparatus. It becomes safer to operate on such a cooled brain. All went well and it was a fascinating experience. Since then, nowadays, there are better and different techniques available to treat such vascular abnormalities of the brain. If not properly dealt with, they usually rebleed, sometimes with a catastrophic outcome.

Dott was a surgical giant of his time, attracting many celebrated medical and other visitors to the department and training by 'apprenticeship' many young doctors from all over the world keen to become neurosurgeons. The torch from Cushing and Halstead was being handed on, internationally, to dedicated, worthy neurosurgeons. The specialty had come of age and indeed was steadily progressing in so many neural spheres in a most dramatic way.

I wish to mention briefly something about Jefferson, Cairns and Penfield.

Professor Sir Geoffrey Jefferson (1886–1961). His doctor father coaxed him to go into medicine. After qualifying, he spent some time in the USA, observing the practice of neurosurgery, but he was really self-taught. He had only two weeks watching Cushing.

He was a brilliant surgeon-philosopher, with a twinkle in his eyes and a fine sense of humour and was well versed in art, literature and poetry. He had few personal trainees.

The Society of British Neurological Surgeons was probably his brain child, being established in the Athenaeum Club in London in 1926. He was also one of the initiators of the World Federation of Neurological Surgeons. He said that 'So long as a man has accomplished something, that is enough.'

I was touched when Professor Dott invited me to visit his home one day, where his good friend 'Geoff' was lying in bed, quite ill. This was a precious visit, to spend some time with this great gentleman, full of kindnesses and wisdom.

Sir Hugh Cairns (1886–1957) differed greatly from both Dott and Jefferson. He was a bluff Australian. He had a travelling fellowship which permitted him to travel to the USA, and this included spending some time with Cushing. In the book by Cairns, *A Study of Intracranial Surgery*, he emphasised that a neurosurgeon must be allowed to decide about admitting patients, to make his own diagnoses and decide on and carry out treatment. His work in World War II was outstanding, and included the development of mobile neurosurgical units.

Dr Wilder Penfield, OM (1889–1976). Like Dott, Penfield received monies from the Rockefeller Foundation to help establish the famous Montreal Neurological Institute (MNI). He had interned at the PBB Hospital in Boston. In 1928 he spent time with the neurosurgeon Otfried Foester in Breslau, gaining significant and valuable interest in epilepsy, which later was to be his main research and clinical involvement, adding greatly to our knowledge of the human brain. He obtained an excellent medical grounding in Oxford, the NHND, Queen Square, and from Sir Charles Sherrington.

His wonderful life story is lovingly set out in his biography *No Man Alone, A Neurosurgeon's Life* (1979). He pioneered a truly comprehensive neurosurgical department, drawing together all the relevant disciplines. He said that linking the brain and the mind is the ultimate problem facing scientists and philosophers.

I was fortunate in spending time in the MNI, studying various aspects of the work on epilepsy, in the laboratories, the wards and the operating theatre. I was very impressed.

Dr and Mrs Penfield were delightful hosts for Sheelagh and me. I kept in touch for many years with Ted Rasmussen and Bill Fiendel, Penfield's two senior neurosurgical associates.

Penfield was an acute observer. He said of Cushing: an impulsive, articulate intellectual, inspired by Osler and Halstead. Of Dott: a cultured technical genius. Of Jefferson: a man of intriguing whimsical philosophies. Of Cairns: a rugged likeable Australian.

Surgical and medical fellowships and the Royal Society of Edinburgh

Post-graduate experience

I have been very fortunate in gaining my post-graduate comprehensive medical and surgical experience from my close involvements with the three Scottish Colleges, medical and surgical. Each organises excellent courses, symposia and lectures, and there is a fine admix of teachers and students.

The Royal Society of Edinburgh is a wonderful forum for high level extramural activities, attracting experts from various academic, cultural, arts, political and business spheres with excellent lectures and symposia, and with links with other institutions in the UK and elsewhere.

To become a surgeon in Britain (really, the United Kingdom – that is, Britain plus Northern Ireland), it is essential to obtain a Fellowship in Surgery from one of the Royal Colleges of Surgeons.

After my demobilisation from the Army in 1948, I was fortunate in obtaining an appointment in the wards of Sir Walter Mercer in the RIE, the aim being to obtain knowledge and experience of various aspects of surgery, including general, orthopaedic, abdominal, urogenital, vascular, neurosurgery, chest, paediatrics, breast, liver and the biliary system, endocrine, metabolic and electrolyte aspects, and trauma. I gained the FRCSE in October 1948.

My sitting, and indeed gaining, the Membership of the Royal College of Physicians of Edinburgh (MRCPE), was the result of the successful persuasion of Professor Dott. He wrote to me during my work at the National Hospital for Nervous Diseases in Queen Square, in London. His reason was that a neurosurgeon (a surgical neurologist) should also be fully familiar with neurology (the work of a medical neurologist). I agreed, but it would require much hard work on my part, to relearn and bring me up to date in the whole of medicine. It was some ten years since I had qualified as a doctor. I made three provisos: to have three months' study leave to enable me to take the Edinburgh Post-Graduate Course in Internal Medicine; to obtain some tuition from Dr Ronald (Ronnie) Robertson, an excellent physician and tutor; and, hopefully to be permitted to attend Professor Sir Derrick Dunlop's famous Sunday clinical ward rounds. All this worked out well. The post-graduate students attending the Internal Medicine Course were surprised and amused, when I, 'one of them' turned up at times as one of their lecturers in neurology!

I gained the MRCPE in July 1954, and later, Dr J. K. Slater, physician and neurologist in the RIE, kindly put my name forward to the College, and in November 1959 I was successful in becoming a Fellow: FRCPE.

In May 1964, Mr J. Sloan Robertson, Consultant neurosurgeon in charge of the neurosurgical department in the West of Scotland (in Killerin Hospital) kindly put my name forward to the Glasgow Royal College of Physicians and Surgeons, and I was accepted, becoming a Fellow, *ad eundem* of that illustrious College. An unexpected honour.

Going 'part-time'

In 1956, a year after becoming a consultant neurosurgeon in Edinburgh, Professor Dott suggested that I should go part-time in the National Health Service (NHS) because I would have more independence. I did not feel that I could afford to do this, but I eventually agreed, knowing that my salary would be reduced by two elevenths. My very first private patient was referred by his general practitioner, who was not happy that the patient had been diagnosed as having multiple sclerosis (MS). My clinical studies and our radiological studies of him revealed a mid-thoracic intervertebral disc protrusion severely compressing the spinal cord. At operation for such a pathology one requires to be extremely careful as the spinal cord in the mid-thoracic region takes up most of the spinal canal; thus retracting the spinal cord can be dangerous, by damaging it. However the offending disc was removed. The outcome was completely satisfactory.

In later times, I approached and removed protruded thoracic intervertebral discs through a transthoracic operative approach.

I add, that by becoming 'part-time', I was permitted to accept and treat overseas patients, as private patients.

(Note: There are 11 half working days in the NHS.)

Being 'head hunted'

On three occasions I have been 'head hunted'.

The first was when I received a telephone call one evening from the neurosurgeon Mr Sloan Robertson, head of the Glasgow neurosurgical unit, established in Killearn Hospital. I was then senior registrar in DCN in Edinburgh. He wished to speak with me about something important. We arranged to meet in his club, the Royal Scottish Automobile Club, in Glasgow. Sipping our whiskies, he said that shortly there would be a vacancy for a consultant neurosurgeon in his unit, and knowing about me was keen that I should apply. He provided me with much information, including the plans for the new department of neurosurgery to be built in the grounds of the Southern General Hospital in Glasgow. I was obviously pleased to hear all this, and thanked him, and would await the advertisement.

However, next day I mentioned the whole affair to Professor Dott, who in his usual quiet, laconic way, said little; just, 'Very nice of Sloan,' but was obviously thinking. Sure enough, Professor Dott then contacted the chairman of the Regional Hospital Board in Edinburgh, and an advertisement for a consultant neurosurgeon for the department of surgical neurology was immediately advertised. Such a situation! Sheelagh and I decided to go for the Edinburgh appointment. I was interviewed, and was successful in obtaining it. I told Mr Sloan Robertson the outcome, and thanked him again for his interest in me.

The next occurred whilst attending a neurosurgical conference in New York, USA, when a gentleman introduced himself, and asked if I would please telephone the Dean of the Mount Sinai hospital and medical school. I did so, and was invited to attend a meeting of a Search Committee, as the Professor of Neurosurgery was retiring and a replacement for him was being sought. I went before this Committee and had a full personal discussion, but neither Sheelagh nor I felt that New York was for us. The Mount Sinai, of course, is a famous medical school and hospital, and has substantial funds.

The third was instigated during an international conference on neurosurgery in Houston, Texas, USA, when an American neurosurgeon approached me and asked if I might be returning to Britain via Boston. In fact we had planned to do so, as Sheelagh has several relations in that city. He said that Professor Sidney Lee, Dean of the Harvard Medical School, would very much like to have a discussion with me. This was arranged, and I had an interesting time with the Dean and the Professor of medical economics, whom he brought in to his office. I was told that, in any event, they were planning to come to Edinburgh to meet with me and certain senior medical people. They sketched out what they had in mind in Boston, replanning and opening up the neurosurgical service in the Peter Bent Brigham Hospital for neurosurgery. That famous hospital is where Dr Harvey Cushing, the father of modern neurosurgery, had worked. A new building and service for VA spinal injury patients was also planned for West Roxbury, Boston. They were seeking a Professor of neurosurgery to take over these hospitals, and I was top of their list. I was flattered and impressed. I would be invited, at Harvard's expense, to spend a week or so in Boston. My return visit there was a busy one, with a well planned programme for me to visit various hospitals and have discussions with medical doctors and others. In addition, I was required to produce my reports and assessments of (a) the overall situation of neurosurgery generally; (b) the situation as I saw it, in Boston; and (c) my projection for the specialty of neurosurgery in the future. I carried out this interesting task.

I was of course in frequent touch by telephone with Sheelagh in Edinburgh, and we came to a decision.

I went before the very distinguished members of the Search Committee, held in the handsome Countway Library of Harvard University. There were many questions and useful discussions. I said how much I appreciated being invited to apply for a Chair of Neurosurgery. It was a most memorable and unique occasion for me. However, considering the situation regarding myself, as an established neurosurgeon in the excellent Department in Edinburgh; and of my wife and young children, and also of my father who was seriously ill; also feeling that it would take considerable time to carry out all of the necessary physical and staffing arrangements, to ensure that the double department of neurosurgery would be entirely satisfactory, I declined. We were well settled in Edinburgh, my native city, which had much to offer us, in so many ways, for medicine, the arts, sporting activities, and schools. Scotland is a beautiful country; yes, the weather could be better but I guess we get used to it. We are also near to many European countries. Was I being a Scottish/Edinburgh chauvinist?

Surgical operating outwith Edinburgh

It is obviously best to operate in your own department, where you know the trained staff, medical and nursing, and your familiar facilities; also where your pre- and post-operative personnel and facilities are to hand.

For particular reasons, I have carried out neurosurgical operations in orthopaedic hospitals in Edinburgh and in Peel Hospital (now the Borders General Hospital), when a combined neurosurgical and orthopaedic procedure was required, with Mr Douglas Lamb, Mr Thomas Whiston or Mr Michael McMaster. I have also worked with Mr Jack Newsam (urological surgeon) and Mr Campbell Buchan (plastic surgeon).

I was invited to demonstrate the 'anterior cervical spine operation' in the Neurosurgical Department in Newcastle. All went well, until we reached the stage where, having removed the offending protruding cervical intervertebral disc which had been compressing a cervical nerve root, the two vertebral bodies were to be grafted with a bone dowel which was removed from the patient's iliac crest. The bone dowel is shaped like a cork, and the dowel was now gently tapped into place, in the hole that had been drilled in the spine. The function of the bone dowel was to fuse the two vertebral bodies, and also to maintain the height between them (the intervertebral disc having been removed), to retain the − necessary − normal size of the intervertebral foramina to ensure that the two cervical nerves at the operated level were not compressed and compromised.

However, either the diameter of the dowel was too small, or the drilled hole was too wide, because, to my consternation, the dowel slipped quite deeply into the hole, possibly deep enough to compress and damage the patient's spinal cord! As was my usual practice for these anterior cervical spine operations, I had carefully measured and had recorded both the depth of the drilled hole and the length of the bony dowel. But, in the circumstances, a lateral radiograph of the patient's neck was taken in the operating theatre; the operation site looked satisfactory. At the end of the operation the patient's clinical neurological state was assessed, and was seen to be quite satisfactory. He showed immediate benefit from the operation. The problem was that the instruments were quite new, being used for the first time, but they would now obviously require to be returned to the manufacturer to have the drill and the dowel cutter carefully checked, and probably be replaced with new, correct instruments. I must say that, even without a gallery of neurosurgeons and neurologists in the operating theatre, I was very worried when that bony dowel went into the hole rather easily!

Fortunately I had no worrying experiences with other 'away from home' operations, including those in the RAMC or in the National Hospital for Nervous Diseases, Queen Square, London. Nor in Athens, Greece; in Cairo, Egypt; or in hospitals in India.

CHAPTER 2

The brain

There is great treasure there behind our skull, and this is true for all of us.
This treasure has great powers, and I would say we only have learned a very
small part of what it can do.

Isaac Basheris Singer

Introduction

MAN'S BRAIN MAKES HIM supreme in our world. It is a remarkable
unique organ protected in a rigid container, the skull, able to do very
much more than the most elaborate, sophisticated electronic computers,
not in speed but in the quite remarkable variety of its many special
functions.

Sir Russell Brain (subsequently, Lord Brain OM), the brilliant medical
neurologist, philosopher and scientist, in his Sir Arthur Stanley Eddington
Memorial Lecture (1959) stated that 'the human brain with its ten million
electrical units, packed into a few cubic inches, is a marvel of electronic
engineering, which scientists can never hope to emulate.'

Particular regions of the brain subserve certain neurological and psychological functions. It is clinically necessary to appreciate these parts, although
they are not actual anatomical lobes. Pathological conditions, such as a brain
tumour or a head injury, usually involve more than a single lobe. Clinical
and imaging studies usually provide in a more precise way the location, size
and nature of the pathology of lesions. Such imaging studies include plain
radiographs, and more importantly, computerised tomography (CT) and
magnetic resonance imaging (MRI) scans; also cerebral angiography and
certain other special studies. Briefly:

(a) *The frontal lobes* are concerned with cognitive functions, intelligence
and emotion, and a lesion there can also cause contralateral motor
hemiparesis. A lesion of the dominant frontal lobe might cause speech
disturbances in the form of expressive dysphasia. Personality, ability to
initiate and social behaviour may also be disturbed by a lesion of these
lobes.

(b) *The temporal lobes* are involved with memory and the emotions. Smell
sensation, hearing, and disturbance of the fields of vision (FOV) may

also be affected by a lesion there, such a lesion causing homonymous hemianopia (HH).

(c) *In the parietal lobes* a lesion may cause receptive dysphasia, and contralateral sensory loss. Pertaining to the dominant parietal lobe, there might also be difficulty with calculations and with the appreciation of objects – their size, shape, weight and texture; also the possibility of HH. Of the non-dominant parietal lobe, lesions can result in difficulty with orientation of the person's body in space, also with problems with dressing, and disturbance of the ability to calculate.

(d) *Occipital lobes* involvement causes a visual field disturbance called hemianopia.

(e) *A cerebellar lesion* can cause the patient to be ataxic.

Hydrocephalus

Our bodies contain a number of essential, very complex systems and mechanisms, vital to our well-being and survival. These include the formation, circulation and absorption of the cerebrospinal fluid (CSF). The CSF is produced by the choroid plexuses, tufts of specialised tissue located mainly in the lateral ventricles in the cerebral hemispheres; yes, in some respects the supreme organ, the brain, is hollow. From there the CSF flows into the third ventricle and down a narrow channel, the aqueduct, into the fourth ventricle, from where it flows over the brain and the spinal cord in a space called the subarachnoid space, and is absorbed by special tissues at the top of the brain (called arachnoid granulations), into the bloodstream. This is going on in each of us, day and night, all of our lives. The CSF serves several purposes and the flow pressure is strictly regulated. If there is physical obstruction at certain sites, there will be a build up of pressure and there can be the development of hydrocephalus (*hydro*: water; *cephals*: the head: 'water in or on the brain'). Proteinous fluids from a spinal neoplasm (or from a cerebral neoplasm) can cause chronic progressive communicating hydrocephalus (Harris, 1962). In babies and early infancy the cranial sutures and the fontanelles are not yet closed, therefore hydrocephalus will cause enlargement of the head, spread of the sutures and bulging of the fontanelles; there are also other signs, as well as symptoms such as vomiting and headache. There can be visual disturbances and examination of the back (fundi) of eyes with an ophthalmoscope will reveal an appearance called papilloedema.

After early infancy the skull is a closed bony container and, except for the changes in the size of the head, the other features just mentioned will become apparent with raised intracranial pressure, from blockage of CSF pathways, from such pathologies as a brain neoplasm, blood clots, swollen (oedematous) brain, or congenital abnormalities.

If the actual cause for the hydrocephalus and raised intracranial pressure cannot be properly dealt with surgically, and the hydrocephalus continues, the patient will become blind, and be increasingly ill, drowsy and unconscious and die. There is a place for some form of operative procedure to direct the CSF either from a lateral ventricle or sometimes, where there is the so-called communicating type of hydrocephalus, from the lumbar subarachnoid space, usually to the abdominal peritoneal space. These procedures are called 'shunts'. I can remember some of the earlier shunting procedures, to direct the CSF to a region where it would be absorbed into the vascular circulation; some of them were quite ingenious, such as using a ureter or the thoracic duct, or the posterior aspect of a vertebral body, the pleural cavity, the mastoid air cells, or a fallopian tube. But these were not successful; nor were attempts to destroy the choroids plexuses. But better drainage systems were developed, incorporating a valve. However there are still other problems, including the growth of a young person to adulthood. Then the shunt system will probably require to be revised.

Head injuries

Head injuries (HI) are common; each year 200–300 people per 100,000 of the population in Western countries are admitted to hospital because of a head injury. About 5 per cent with a severe HI, usually having multiple intracranial pathological changes such as haemorrhages, lacerations, and swelling (oedema), will be in coma, and will probably die. A patient with a less severe head injury can have pathological lesions such as an intracranial haematoma (clot of blood); a linear or a depressed fracture of the skull; a leakage of CSF from the nose or an ear; or a compound fracture of the skull which will certainly occur from a penetrating HI, including bullets and shrapnel.

The commonest cause for a head injury, certainly in Western countries, is a road traffic accident. Other causes include falls or assaults during certain contact sports such as football (soccer) and rugby; diving into water; horse riding. There can be associated injuries, especially to the neck; but also to limbs, the chest, abdomen, pelvis and to thoracic and lumbar regions of the spine.

The location and the scene of the accident will obviously determine the action to be taken by the people who are present. If the head injury appears to be serious, emergency medical help, paramedical, and ambulance personnel will be required. Meanwhile first aid measures are necessary. Control obvious external bleeding, ensure a free airway, examine the patient and record your findings, even briefly; and recheck the findings (that is, the patient's clinical state) about one to two hourly. Check his conscious state, the response to speech and commands, the use of limbs, the size and reaction to light of the pupils, and the volume and rate of the pulse.

There is an important special head injury chart, the Glasgow Coma Scale (GCS), whereby the level of consciousness may be assessed. It includes the clinical study of the patient's eyes, the best motor response, and the best verbal (speech) response.

Find out if the patient has taken alcohol or/and drugs.

If he is unconscious, and is on his back, very, very gently roll him over on to his side, appreciating that there could be an associated neck injury (cervical spine). This position should facilitate breathing, and prevent aspiration of vomitus.

Prevention of a head injury includes the use of proper, official seat belts in vehicles, and suitable seats to allow proper head and neck support. Driving should be good and careful. Motor cyclists and bicyclists must wear proper, official helmets. In the house, there should be adequate lighting and good carpeting. Special coaching and sensible care are needed when involved in potentially dangerous sports. Consider the very real dangers of alcohol!

Some personal examples of patients with a head injury:

Late one night we received an urgent telephone call from a Consultant general surgeon in a general hospital far distant from Edinburgh. A patient who had sustained a severe closed head injury had been admitted there. He was becoming increasingly drowsy and had developed weakness of the left side of his body. Skull X-rays showed a linear fracture of the right temporal bone. The right temporalis muscle was boggy. There had been a brief period of loss of consciousness initially, then a lucid interval and a return of depressed consciousness. This was a typical example of a traumatic extradural haemorrhage – bleeding into the head between the strong covering of the brain, the dura and the skull, most probably from a traumatic rupture of an artery – the middle meningeal artery in relation to the fracture of the right temporal bone. Such a condition is a real, serious, emergency, as further bleeding could quite quickly cause an enlarging clot – a haematoma – and seriously compress and dislocate the patient's brain;

and if not urgently treated, there would be a fatal outcome. The referring surgeon was unfamiliar with the practical management of such a condition. Immediate surgical treatment was required. We therefore advised the surgeon immediately to contact the hospital joiner or engineer and obtain a drill, a brace and bits, and to sterilise them. Under local anaesthetic he should make one or two drill (burr) holes in the right temporal bone. Some of the extradural clot and liquid blood would escape under pressure. He should wash more clot out with sterile normal saline and use suction. Our Senior Neurosurgical Registrar had been dispatched with appropriate sterile instruments. He would then ensure that all of the haematoma had been removed, and had obtained haemostasis. He closed the wounds, then carefully assessed the patient's clinical state and advised about subsequent management. All went well. Subsequently we arranged for surgeons in outlying hospitals to visit our Department and see and be taught about the practical management of certain head injury patients.

Head injuries and golf

My father, a very keen golfer, was enjoying a game at Kilspindie golf course, near Edinburgh, with his great friend, a naval Captain, and myself. Out of the blue came a golf ball, striking the Captain on the head, with no yell of 'fore'. He was felled, but was only briefly unconscious. Indeed he stood up, and we heard a remarkable long flow of naval invective, stating what he thought of the offending player!

A fatal fall

A middle aged gentleman slipped on an icy pavement and landed heavily on the pavement, striking his head. There was immediate loss of consciousness. He was quite quickly seen by paramedics and ambulance personnel, who ensured that the patient had a good airway, that there was no external bleeding, nor any obvious associated injuries. Pulse, respirations and blood pressure were recorded and the patient was rapidly brought to our Department. However, he was showing evidence of a neurological state called decerebration, which is invariably a terminal condition. He had cardio-respiratory arrest, and died almost immediately on being admitted. The autopsy showed extensive, serious damage to his brain, with haemorrhages, lacerations and swelling.

A most tragic case, from 'just a fall'.

Just a bang on the head

A man of sixty accidentally knocked his head slightly whilst getting into a friend's car. He was a little dizzy and had slight headache. As time went on, indeed after some weeks, he developed more definite, poorly localised headaches, becoming a little confused and rather drowsy. His GP understandably was concerned and was suspicious of an intracranial pathology, referring him to our department.

The history, along with the clinical findings of raised intracranial pressure, shown by the presence of bilateral papilloedema (seen by using an ophthalmoscope: swelling of the disc and fullness of the retinal veins), a mild right-sided hemiparesis, slurred indistinct speech, and fluctuating drowsiness, was classical for the presence of a post-traumatic, chronic subdural haematoma. The diagnosis was confirmed by an imaging study. The course of events would be the minor closed head injury causing tearing of veins coursing from the surface of the left cerebral hemisphere to enter the superior longitudinal sinus (then into the general venous circulation to the heart). There would be seepage of blood into the subdural space in the head; that is, a chronic subdural haematoma. There occurs a steady, further accumulation of blood causing the symptoms and signs aforementioned. In some older people there is a degree of cerebral atrophy permitting an increase in the haematoma, compressing and displacing the brain. If not dealt with surgically, the patient would become comatose and die from the effects of increasing intracranial pressure.

The treatment is straightforward. Make two or three cranial burr holes over the side of the head, where the haematoma is likely to be located, as shown by the clinical and radiological findings, and evacuate the haematoma. This will leave quite a significant gap – a large space between the brain and the duramater. My practice then has been, with the patient on his side on the operating table, to do a lumbar puncture and introduce a quantity of Ringer's solution (it is like CSF) under moderate pressure, to float the brain up and close off the subdural space where the haematoma was, to discourage re-accumulation of fluid (this is the procedure introduced by Dr Gardner of the Cleveland Clinic). Also, for about two or three days the patient is kept tilted head down in his bed. The results of such treatment for a chronic subdural haematoma are usually excellent.

A road accident

Some while ago, on returning by car from a golfing visit to Turnberry, the traffic was going very slowly indeed. Something must have happened ahead. Sure enough, as we (my wife and I) neared a crashed private car we saw a man lying on the side of the road, quite still, and bleeding freely from a large scalp wound. I got out and applied clean handkerchiefs wrapped around tightly with two ordinary ties. This stopped the loss of blood. He was unconscious, obviously from a severe head injury, but there was no obvious limb weakness and the pupils were normal. He had a weak, rapid pulse. We turned him on to his side. Breathing was normal. There was no obvious evidence of any associated injury. After about ten minutes an ambulance arrived with ambulance men and paramedics and the patient was whisked off to a nearby hospital.

I could hardly believe that the onlookers were just standing around, and looking, up to the time we came on the scene! The poor man could have died!

An injured orang-utan

The Director of the Edinburgh Zoo telephoned me to ask if I could possibly, quite urgently, come to the Zoo, as their wonderful orang-utan had been found unconscious in his cage, beside his mate. I was interested, but at first wondered if this could be a hoax. However I went to the Zoo, and found the animal to be drowsy with a large haematoma (blood clot) under the scalp, most probably a skull fracture. There were no other obvious neurological signs. I spoke with the head keeper and the Director, advising a careful watch on the animal and mentioning the Glasgow Coma Scale. I visited the Zoo each day, and was pleased that there was improvement. One day after using my ophthalmoscope to see if there was evidence of raised intracranial pressure, the orang-utan literally aped me, by prising open the keeper's eyelids and looking in! Fortunately there was a full neurological recovery, but in our Department there was the expected joke – a photograph of the animal alongside a photograph of me, the caption saying, 'On the right is Mr Harris'!

Head injuries in childhood

In a study I carried out on a consecutive series of patients, in a five-year period, of 150 children and 450 adults who had been admitted to our

Department because of a head injury, some interesting differences were found comparing the two groups.

The children had a lower morbidity and mortality, and had greater reorganisation of neurological and psychological functions. Recovery from similar types of head injury appeared to be more rapid and complete in the young patients. Dr J. A. L. Naughton, MC, clinical neuropsychologist, carried out the psychological studies. It was interesting that if the brain injury occurred at an early age (before two years), and involved the dominant (that is, usually the left) cerebral hemisphere, several of these patients became left-handed and developed speech normally.

Twenty-six per cent of the children developed post-traumatic epilepsy; twelve had not had an initial period of unconsciousness associated with the head injury.

Thirteen per cent had persistent psychological changes. Eleven had an extradural haematoma. The ages varied from 4 to 11 years. Four of these patients died from the brain injury.

Twenty-five per cent of the adults had a 'typical post-concussional syndrome' compared to only 6 per cent in children.

Intracranial neoplasms

Definition:

- *A neoplasm* (*neo* – something new (Greek) and *plasm* – the living nature of a cell (Latin): a new formation of tissue in some part of the body. A tumour.
- *A tumour* (Latin origin of the word) – a swelling, a mass, a swollen condition, a morbid swelling.
- *A growth* – a morbid formation.

A malignant tumour

A young man was urgently referred from his GP with a short medical history of two to three months of increasingly severe headaches, not well localised, and the gradual but then more rapid development of a left hemiparesis and drowsiness. He was admitted forthwith. Clinical examination showed him to be very drowsy but able when stimulated to co-operate with the examination. He had a moderately severe left sided hemiparesis and sensory changes, brisk deep reflexes, extensor (abnormal) plantar reflexes, and a marked degree of papilloedema.

The history and the clinical neurological findings certainly pointed to the presence of a rapidly growing tumour involving the right cerebral hemisphere. This was confirmed by the imaging studies that our radiologist carried out. The outlook looked poor, but the situation was discussed with the patient and his family, having been told of the seriousness of the condition. The decision was taken for the patient to have a cranial operation, with the hope that, when the histology of the tumour was known − by an immediate frozen section biopsy − a palliative, partial removal of the tumour could be carried out. However, the craniotomy showed that there was a large malignant glioma involving the right fronto-parietal region of the brain, and that the tumour had extended to involve the main connecting fibres of the brain − the corpus callosum − invading part of the opposite, the left cerebral hemisphere. It was a terrible situation.

He became increasingly drowsy, with a complete left hemiplegia. He did not respond to any medical measures, and within a week became comatose.

A benign tumour

The patient had experienced headaches for some months − thought possibly to be due to migraine, but not responding well to non-addictive analgesic tablets, nor to anti-migrainous medicines. The headaches had become more prominent, and then there were two spaced fits. These were focal, called Jacksonian fits (epilepsy), and with the second, there was some weakness of the right arm, leg and side of the face, also difficulty in getting words out − that is, expressive dysphasia. These neurological changes are called Todd's paresis, and are usually a temporary phenomenon. All of this was confirmed on admission, when also we found evidence of raised intracranial pressure, as examination of the patient's eyes with an ophthalmoscope showed quite definite papilloedema. The diagnosis was most probably an intracranial neoplasm involving the left side of the brain. An imaging study, an angiogram, confirmed the likely diagnosis − a large, very vascular meningioma, compressing but not infiltrating the left upper convex fronto-parietal region of the brain.

At operation, the very vascular growth was defined, and was completely excised. Post-operative state was quite satisfactory. We could not guarantee that the fits would be controlled, but follow-up examinations, including EEG (electroencephalogram) studies over three years were quite satisfactory, and the anti-epileptic drugs were gradually discontinued.

Extracerebral tumours

Meningiomas make up about 20 per cent of all brain tumours. They arise from cells of the arachnoid which closely covers the brain, under the tough covering, the dura. They grow slowly, are usually very vascular, and form an enlarging mass which indents the underlying brain. The clinical presentation is usually one of headaches, and slowly developing increasing focal neurological changes, depending on the location. Epilepsy can occur. Once the diagnosis, location and the vascularity of the tumour have been confirmed and shown by imaging studies, the neurosurgeon will operate and totally excise the mass. The prognosis is usually very good.

Acoustic neurinomas make up about 5 per cent of primary intracranial neoplasms, arising from the 8th (acoustic, auditory) cranial nerve. Growth is usually very slow, forming a solid, moderately vascular mass, extending from the innermost aspect of the inner ear in the skull to the pons, part of the brainstem, and being closely associated with the 7th (facial) and 5th (trigeminal) cranial nerves. Thus the symptoms can include loss of hearing (deafness), tinnitus (a sensation of ringing in the head), and vertigo (a sensation of whirling, giddiness, dizziness, and a tendency to lose one's balance). With increased growth can come also ipsilateral weakness of the facial muscles of expression (7th nerve), and ipsilateral cutaneous facial loss (5th nerve); and eventually, if not yet treated, there can be increased intracranial pressure, causing hydrocephalus.

Clinical and imaging studies will confirm the diagnosis.

Treatment is by complete excision of the tumour. This can be quite challenging for the neurosurgeon if the mass is large.

Intracerebral tumours

About 50 per cent of these are *metastatic tumours* (usually multiple) from, in particular, the lung or the breast. There is usually a very poor prognosis.

Gliomas make up 25 per cent of all intracranial tumours, arising from the glia, the supporting cells of the brain. There are different grades. The astrocytoma grows slowly to begin with but then may have a rapid growth, and is then called a malignant glioma or, another name, glioblastoma multiforme. These latter tumours grow very rapidly indeed, over a matter of several weeks. Depending on their location in the brain, and the speed of the growth, there can be several clinical syndromes, and headaches and raised intracranial pressure are usually present. Imaging studies are essential, to provide the diagnosis, location and size. Some show a cystic change. The management concerns the neurosurgeon and an oncologist. For slow growing astrocytomas, an operation is indicated, to excise, or sometimes it may only be possible to partially excise, the growth. Such measures may have a reasonable, guarded prognosis. The outlook is bleak for patients harbouring a malignant glioma.

However in young children an astrocytoma arising from the part of the brain called the cerebellum can have a good prognosis from treatment. This is also the case for another type of glioma seen in young children, arising in the roof of the 4th ventricle, called a medulloblastoma.

The pituitary gland

(A) Tumours

The pituitary gland is small, weighing only about 500 mg, and is strategically and neatly located in a fossa in the base of the skull, under the brain, being connected by a stalk to part of the brain called the hypothalamus, and superior to the gland are the two optic nerves and the optic chiasm.

It produces essential hormones, and has been referred to as 'the leader of the endocrine orchestra', because of its vital hormonal links with several other hormone glands in the body.

What follows is a very brief mention of some of the very important and fascinating conditions that can result from over or under secretion of pituitary gland hormones; and the possible effects on the optic nerves and chiasm causing significant disturbances of vision by large adenomas (these are non-malignant). It will be obvious that close cooperation by the neurosurgeon with fellow specialists, especially in endocrinology, neuro-ophthalmology and neuroradiology, is absolutely essential in the diagnosis and management of pituitary disorders.

About 15 per cent of all intracranial tumours are pituitary tumours.

The adenomas

1. Eosinophilic adenomas produce excess of growth hormone, and in adults cause acromegaly (Greek: enlargement of the extremities) with characteristic body changes, including enlargement of the head and facial features and of the hands and feet, muscular hypertrophy, headaches and often also disturbances of vision, such as bitemporal hemianopia and later indeed, if untreated, complete blindness. In young people, before the

long bones have stopped growing, the remarkable condition of gigantism appears along with many of the features just mentioned. Indeed, did the giant mentioned in the Bible have acromegaly and so be unable to see David's stone coming?

2. Basophilic adenomas are quite small and are rare. They occur more commonly in women. Excess of pituitary adenocorticotrophine hormone (ACTH) stimulates the adrenal gland (situated in the abdomen) production of cortisol, causing a striking disorder called Cushing's disease, with serious body changes. There is a strong link with the adrenal glands.

3. Prolactinomas are usually very small, producing excess of prolactin, resulting in hypogonadism; and in females, galactorrhoea, amenorrhoea and infertility.

4. Chromophobe (non-secretory) adenomas cause failure of all of the pituitary hormones, with amenorrhoea; and in males failure of libido and potency; also striking body changes (Simmond's disease).

Management of patients with pituitary adenomas

Having been thoroughly studied and investigated by the neurosurgeon, endocrinologist, ophthalmologist and neuroradiologist, a decision is taken about the best treatment for the patient. The neurosurgical operative approach will be either by a formal frontal craniotomy, or by a transphenoidal approach. Treatment by specialised deep X-radiation is sometimes indicated as a primary measure. A better irradiation treatment is the insertion of radioactive Yttrium 90 (Y^{90}) rods into the tumour by a transphenoidal operation. Y^{90} is a beta-particle emitter of high energy and a short half life. Expert endocrinological management is essential, before and subsequent to the elective treatment.

Pituitary gland ablation (hypophysectomy)

It was found, fortuitously, that a lady who had diabetes and who developed post-partum hypopituitarism had a striking benefit in her diabetic retinopathy (DR). This was reported; and also some experimental studies showed marked improvement on DR, and therefore in visual functions, after hypophysectomy.

Frontal craniotomy for pituitary ablation was a major procedure for people with vision-threatening DR; their severe diabetes usually having significant general vascular disturbances, and therefore was not without risk.

In the Western Infirmary in Glasgow, Mr (later, Professor Sir Patrick) Forrest devised a procedure, using the transphenoidal operative route (through the nose and base of the skull), inserting radioactive radon seeds, mainly for selected patients with advanced breast cancer. But a better technique to ablate the pituitary gland was devised in his Department, inserting rods of radioactive Yttrium 90 (Y^{90}) into the pituitary gland.

In Edinburgh, treating patients with serious, vision-threatening DR, we first carried out operations to section the pituitary stalk, but this involved a major neurosurgical, frontal craniotomy, not without risk for these diabetically ill patients; also complete pituitary gland ablation could not always be obtained. Pat Forrest kindly invited me over to his Department and the radio-active Y^{90} technique was demonstrated. I was impressed, and our team of specialists in Edinburgh (ophthalmologist, neurosurgeon, endocrinologist and neuroradiologist) carried out the procedure in over twenty patients, all with severe DR and failing vision. Immaculate pre- and post-operative specialist management is necessary. Our first publication was in 1965, and the next, with careful follow-up studies, in 1971. We found that complete pituitary ablation was necessary. Arrest, and in some patients actual regression of the threatening loss of vision, was obtained.

We also treated a small number of patients with advanced breast cancer, also some with acromegaly, with radio-active Y^{90} (it has a half life of 64 hours), and we also began to use cryosurgery for pituitary ablation.

Vascular disorders

Middle cerebral artery aneurysm

He was a forty-year-old highly intelligent gentleman, who had been dux of Glasgow Academy and was a Cambridge University graduate, a well known writer and journalist, and at one time a Scottish Nationalist Member of Parliament. One evening in October 1979, when watching television, he lost consciousness and fell, and was amnesic for three days. His doctor had him admitted to our department. There was bilateral papilloedema, and a mild right hemiparesis. Cerebral angiography revealed a left middle cerebral artery aneurysm. At operation the neck of aneurysm was occluded with a Mayfield clip. He did well following the operation, but developed communicating hydrocephalus, which is not uncommonly encountered in patients with subarachnoid haemorrhage, because of blockage of the draining villi of the superior sagittal venous sinus by blood. This condition was dealt with by an operation, inserting a valve/shunt to by-pass the blockage of the villi, and thus allowing the cerebrospinal fluid (CSF) to drain away into the vascular circulation.

A few weeks later, at follow-up, he was neurologically intact. He asked if he could start refereeing rugby matches again and was told that he could even take up playing again soon if he wanted. I had forgotten that this interesting, erudite, athletic individual was also a mountaineer. I told him that if he wished, he could begin hill-walking; but when we next met, I found that he had been climbing the foothills of Mount Everest! (*Douglas Crawford 1939–2002. Tributes and Medical Writings*. Compiled by Avril Anderson, East Kilbride, Scotland. 2004.)

Cerebral aneurysms

An aneurysm (from the Greek) is a morbid dilatation of an artery or a vein owing to disease or a tumour, caused by rupture of the arterial coats. (One would add, or from a congenital or developmental cause.)

Cerebral aneurysms result from a developmental weakness of the media part of the wall of an artery. They are usually saccular, are about the size of a small pea or a berry, and most have a 'neck' where they arise from their parent cerebral artery, part of the circle of Willis – a ring of arteries situated at the under surface of the brain (Harris P. and Udvarheyli G.B. 1957). Such aneurysms usually, sooner or later, rupture, causing the well known condition of subarachnoid haemorrhage, with sudden, acute headache, neck stiffness, and photophobia. There may be drowsiness (even sudden death) and other neurological changes, depending on the location of the aneurysm, and there is often localised arterial spasm. There can be more than one aneurysm in the individual patient; my 'record' is six – obviously causing therapeutic problems. There can be premonitory quite mild headaches.

Prompt clinical diagnosis is essential, with rapid admission to a Department of Neurosurgery, because there is a strong chance of a recurrent bleed from what is likely to be a cerebral aneurysm; then there could be serious brain damage, and even a fatal outcome if a cerebral aneurysm rebleeds. The diagnosis will be confirmed by the history, the clinical findings and by contrast x-rays, cerebral angiography. In my time, a direct approach to the aneurysm by a craniotomy was the procedure to treat the aneurysm, with the invaluable help of the dissecting microscope, to clip occlude the aneurysm neck, or by some other surgical procedure to ensure that the aneurysm would not rebleed. Nowadays some skilled neuro-radiologists are able to treat certain cerebral aneurysms (and also certain arteriovenous malformations (AVM)) by an endovascular operative procedure.

Cerebral arteriovenous malformations (AVM)

These are congenital and are composed of a complex of arteries and veins, usually forming a wedge-shaped mass of vascular tissues; the apex of the wedge usually lies deep in the brain. They are of variable size and will, apparently, sooner or later bleed. They may cause epilepsy. Once diagnosed, they require to be excised; this can be formidable.

Occlusive vascular disease

An elderly individual, in 'pretty good shape generally', had a history of three, recurrent, spaced, transient ischaemic attacks (TIAs). For them, he was receiving aspirin, but with the last TIA there was continuing weakness of the right side of the body, and expressive dysphasia. When admitted to the Department of Neurosurgery, the medical history and the clinical findings were confirmed. The patient was fully alert and cooperative on clinical examination. The blood pressure was also normal and the heart sounds were closed (normal). Auscultation of the neck revealed a loud bruit (noise) over the left internal carotid/common carotid artery region. Carotid angiography showed a markedly stenotic (narrowed) left internal carotid artery. The patient was shown the angiograms (contrast X-ray studies obtained by injecting a radio-opaque fluid into the carotid arteries in the neck), and there was a clear necessity for an operation on the pathological damaged artery, to prevent further TIAs, and indeed prevent the development of a complete right sided hemiplegia and severe dysphasia. The patient agreed to have the operation, which was quite straightforward, consisting of a left internal carotid artery endarterectomy – opening the vessel and removing the atheromatous degenerate material, thus maintaining the normal vascular lumen. The result was quite satisfactory, and was seen on routine out-patient follow-up examinations.

(i) Transient ischaemic attacks (TIAs)

The above mentioned case provides the main information about these common attacks, affecting older people.

Atherosclerotic changes occurring in the carotid arteries (and which can also occur in the vertebral arteries causing a syndrome such as 'drop attacks') can stenose (narrow) them, and small pieces of an atheromatous plaque can also break away, forming an embolus, and be lodged in a cerebral artery, causing neurological changes.

(ii) Intracerebral haemorrhage; and cerebral thrombosis: causing a 'stroke'

Strokes appear to be the single biggest cause for major disability in the UK (Martin, Meltzer and Elliot: 1998); and the third leading cause of death in most Western countries.

Strokes mainly occur in older people, and hypertension (high blood pressure), and diabetes are often important factors.

The haemorrhage or, from a cerebral thrombosis, the cerebral infarction (which is death of part of the brain due to vascular occlusion), involves the deep part of a cerebral hemisphere, usually causing a sudden (thus the term, 'stroke') episode, with contralateral hemiplegia and altered consciousness. About a third of such patients will succumb in less than a week. The illness appears dramatically, and is very serious, demanding urgent medical attention: ensure that there is a free airway; aspirin may be given initially; check the pulse and blood pressure; ambulance staff and paramedics will probably be involved, but the most important action is for the patient to be admitted to the best possible main hospital, particularly to an acute, specialist stroke unit; or to the very nearest equivalent. Time is of the essence; up-to-date, appropriate treatment must be given within three hours of the onset of the stroke-illness.

We were fortunate in having a superb (MRC) special stroke unit in our Department, under Professor Warlow. These patients initially (and indeed also subsequently) come under the special care of consultant medical neurologists and consultant neuroradiologists. Neurosurgeons may never be consulted. To begin with the clot (haematoma), deep in the brain, is semifluid and is surrounded by soft, oedematous (swollen) brain; at this stage, no attempt should be made to stop the bleeding or to deal with the clot. However, later, if the clot becomes more confined and brain oedema has settled, neurosurgical removal of the clot could be considered.

Intracranial infections

Before the wonderful discovery of penicillin by Fleming, followed by the discovery and the availability of other antibiotics, intracranial infections,

9. *Dr John Orr, Dean of the Medical School*

10. *Professor Norman M. Dott.* Courtesy of Royal College of Surgeons, Edinburgh

11. A Nightingale ward: Royal Infirmary of Edinburgh

12. Professor Sir John Fraser. Courtesy of Royal College of Surgeons, Edinburgh

13. Lieutenant in the Royal Army Medical Corps (RAMC), aged 23 years

14. Professor Sir Derrick Dunlop. Courtesy of Royal College of Physicians, Edinburgh

15. *Professor Sir Walter Mercer.* Courtesy of Royal College of Surgeons, Edinburgh

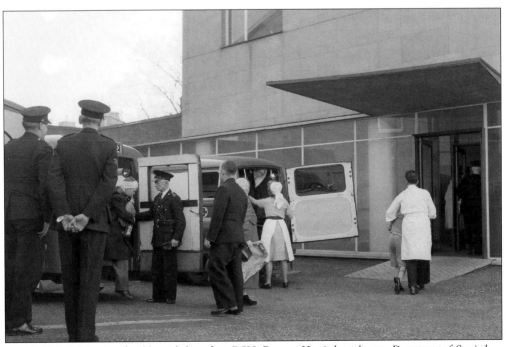

16. *Patients being transferred by ambulance from DSN, Bangour Hospital, to the new Department of Surgical Neurology (DSN) building, Western General Hospital, 1960.* Courtesy of The Scotsman Publications Ltd, Edinburgh

17. Harvey Cushing (right in the photograph) and Otfried Foester. Courtesy of British Medical Association, Publishing Group, London. *J Neurol. Neurosurg. Psychiat.* 1985, 48: 965–976

18. *Operation in progress in the Department of Surgical Neurology, Western General Hospital, Edinburgh.* Courtesy of National Health Service, Lothian

19. Professor Sir Geoffrey Jefferson. Courtesy of British Medical Association, Publishing Group, London. *J. Neurol. Neurosurg. Psychiat.* 1985, 48: 965–976

20. Sister Rhoda Kerr, my Senior Ward Nursing Sister

and in particular brain abscess or indeed multiple brain abscesses, were commonly encountered, and required urgent diagnosis and neurosurgical treatment, often with a serious outcome, sometimes fatal.

In more recent times such serious infections are not often seen. Primary sources for the infection are infections from the middle ear, the mastoid or the paranasal air sinuses, or from facial or scalp infections, pulmonary infections, or a compound skull fracture. It could come from the infection of a cranial, brain operation site. Clinical and imaging studies provide the diagnosis. Treatment is urgently required: antibiotics and anti-brain oedema (swelling) drugs, and neurosurgical drainage of the abscess or abscesses, sometimes their excision. Unfortunately, epilepsy is a common complication of cerebral abscess.

Reduction of operative haemorrhage

Induced arterial hypotension, and induced hypothermia

Certain cerebral lesions are very vascular and present a special challenge to the neurosurgeon when operating on them. The pathologies in particular are some very vascular tumours, usually meningiomas, complex arterio-venous malformations, and some unusual aneurysms of the brain.

In our department we have used both the procedures of *induced arterial hypotension*, and also *induced hypothermia*.

For the former one uses hypotensive drugs, or gives the patient a high spinal anaesthetic, to paralyse the pre-gangliomic sympathetic fibres, the aim being to obtain a systolic blood pressure (BP) of about 60 mm of mercury. The effect can be maintained for about three hours. Another somewhat unusual procedure that we have used is that of arteriotomy: controlled bleeding of the patient is carried out, the arterial blood being stored in sterile bottles in the operating theatre, and the blood is returned to the patient later during the operation. With a lowered BP very vascular tissues are easier and safer to handle and deal with surgically.

Induced hypothermia can provide, literally, a bloodless field for the neurosurgeon, but like induced hypotension, is also not without risk, and is only to be used by those fully familiar with the special techniques and the indications, and bearing in mind the risk of possible complications.

Reduction of the oxygen requirements of the brain and of metabolism occurs, with the oesophageal temperature lowered and maintained at 30°C, and the BP and the intracranial cerebrospinal fluid pressures becoming lowered. This can be achieved by giving certain drugs, such as 'a lytic cocktail', or by internal or external applications of ice-cold water to the surface of the body.

Haemostasis in surgery

Because of the soft, friable nature of the brain and the spinal cord, haemostasis using haemostatic (artery) forceps and ligation of vessels as is commonly used in general surgery, is not applicable in neurosurgery. The blood vessels are mainly quite small. Deliberate, meticulous control of bleeding is absolutely essential.

Electrocoagulation with surgical diathermy is absolutely necessary in neurosurgery. Unipolar coagulation is commonly used, but bipolar coagulation, which was devised by Greenwood, permits a circumscribed, pin-point, more accurately controlled lesion for haemostasis, and is certainly essential in microneurosurgery.

I was a member of the British Standards Institute Committee on Surgical Diathermy Apparatus. Our work was published in the *Handbook on Surgical Diathermy*, 1978.

Sheelagh and I had the pleasure of staying with Dr and Mrs Greenwood in Houston, Texas, and had good conversations on a variety of neurosurgical topics, including the several inventions of James Greenwood. We also played some golf.

For haemostasis in neurosurgery, electrocoagulation is often supplemented by using silver clips or gelatin foam, also small pieces of crushed muscle or bone wax (but, better, Absele).

It is interesting that Harvey Cushing with the physicist Bovie introduced electrodiathermy into neurosurgery; Cushing discussed this in his Macewen Memorial Lecture in Glasgow in 1927.

Lasers

The word 'laser' is an acronym for 'Light amplification by stimulated emission of radiation'.

In 1917 Einstein in his quantum theory of radiation theoretically foresaw the possibility of the stimulated emission of light whereby a stimulated photon could be made to release a second photon as it decays to a lower energy state (Einstein 1954). The photons must be contained, harnessed and controlled.

In the 1960s the first laser, the ruby laser, was applied medically by Maiman.

I knew about lasers, and also about the CUSA instrument, and felt that both should become available, as soon as possible, in our Department of Neurosurgery in Edinburgh. We should always be at the forefront of new ideas and techniques.

A good friend, Mr Philip Mackie, Deputy Editor of the *Edinburgh Evening News* headed an important charity run by that paper, and monies were being received from readers and others. We were very fortunate in receiving grants from that source, which allowed us to purchase both a laser apparatus (£24,000), and a CUSA machine (£65,000). We received them in December 1983: probably the first such machines in Scotland, I understand.

I was invited to join the Laser Research Unit in the Heriot Watt University in Edinburgh, headed by Dr M. J. Colles. An Edinburgh laser was being developed, incorporating a carbon dioxide laser with an Nd:Yag laser. In surgical operations, the laser permits precise ablation of tissues, and in particular of tumour cells. Certain operations can be performed more speedily and more safely. There is good healing of tissues with minimal swelling and scarring. Lasers can be cost-effective. The carbon dioxide laser is useful for many brain and spinal cord operations for tumour removal.

I had been wondering if the intravenous injection of a haematoporphyrin derivative (HPD) would be taken up by malignant cerebral glioma tumours, and when the obvious mass of the growth had been removed, probably by the use of a CUSA aspirator, if any remnants of tumour still remaining would be 'identified' by the HPD and then be destroyed by the laser.

CUSA

CUSA is the acronym for 'cosmetic ultrasound surgical aspirator'. It is an elegant precision surgical tool, which surgeons quickly learn to use. Diseased tissue, such as various types of brain or spinal neoplasms, is whipped up by the extremely rapid revolving tip of the machine, to reach the consistency of cream, and is then sucked away.

Epilepsy

Epilepsy (which in distant times was called the 'Sacred Disease', or the falling sickness) is a fascinating and very serious symptom-complex, inclusive of so many important medical and social aspects, necessitating the involvement of a wide range of professional people, including medical doctors, clinical and basic research, and many others in specialist spheres in our society. Temkin (1971) in his book *The Falling Sickness* observes that several famous people had epilepsy, including Dostoievski, whose fits began with an ecstatic aura, going on to grand-mal seizures; in his writings, in *Demons*, the hero, Kirilov, and in *The Idiot*, Prince Myshkin, are saintly types. In *The Brothers Karamasov*, Smerdyako is a murderer. Temkin notes that Caesar, St Paul, Lincoln, Petrach, Charles I, Mahomet, Molière, Peter the Great, Handel, Swift, Richelieu, Flaubert and Byron had epilepsy. Indeed, any person can have epilepsy.

During a Saturday afternoon whilst watching a rugby league game on television, one player had been knocked over and was lying on the field. The commentator said that the player had 'mild concussion', but the TV camera had zoomed down and I saw the player having a major grand-mal epileptic fit. He was taken off the field. This was an example of early post-traumatic epilepsy.

One of my main interests and involvements in neurosurgery is epilepsy, which affects 0.5 to 1.0 per cent of the population some time during their lives. It is not a disease, but is a symptom-complex of several different conditions, with a variety of pathologies and aetiologies, electroencephalogram abnormalities (see the item on the Hans Berger Centenary Symposium on Epilepsy), imaging (including X-ray and brain scan) changes and clinical abnormalities; and necessitating various therapies. Only a small number of people with epilepsy would be considered for special neurological investigations leading up to a neurosurgical operation.

The neurophysiology is complex; a focal group of cells in the grey matter of the brain suddenly undergo electro-chemical changes. The abnormality may remain reasonably confined and quickly subside and there may be EEG changes and possibly also an epileptic fit. But there can be excessive spread to other cerebral areas, resulting in a different form of epilepsy.

A Standard International Classification of Epilepsy became available in 1981, and includes:

(1) Partial seizures: with no loss of consciousness; seizure begins locally; there may be motor, somatosensory or special sensory symptoms; autonomic symptoms; psychic symptoms. The commonest origins are within the frontal or temporal lobes of the brain. With temporal lobe disturbance there can be abnormalities of taste and smell – usually unpleasant for the patient.

(2) Generalised seizures: The commonest type is the tonic-clonic (grand-mal) fit; this may be preceded by an aura experienced by the patient. Also included in this group are petit-mal (absence) fits.

Status epilepticus pertains to the recurrence of tonic-clonic fits without consciousness recovering between the attacks. This is a serious medical emergency and can be fatal.

There are many causes of epilepsy, for example in relation to a head injury; a brain tumour; a vascular lesion such as an infarction or a haemorrhage (e.g. from a cerebral aneurysm or an arteriovenous abnormality); or from infection (e.g. a brain abscess), meningitis or encephalitis. Certain systemic disturbances, such as fever, hypoglycaemia, certain drugs, renal or hepatic factors or respiratory failure, may also be involved. However, in a significant number of patients with epilepsy no obvious, definite cause is found, and thus the term 'idiopathic epilepsy' is used. This is mainly seen in young people.

I have been fortunate in studying various aspects of epilepsy, with the invaluable assistance of grants, including one from the Scottish Epilepsy Society, and one from the McRobert Trust. I visited and studied in some major neurological and neurosurgical centres where epilepsy was being specially studied: Bristol, England; Dr Sem-Jacobsen, Oslo, Norway; Dr Wilder Penfield, Montreal Neurological Institute; Professor A. Earl Walker, John Hopkins University and Medical School.

As the neurosurgical member of the Medical Research Council (MRC) Brain Metabolism Unit (BMU) in the University of Edinburgh, I participated in animal researches there on epilepsy, using implants of (non-radioactive) cobalt, a technique called 'kindling' to produce epilepsy. The findings showed that a 'mirror focus' developed on the opposite half of the brain. Special electrocorticographic studies were done, and a computerised analogue-digital conversion technique was used. Removal of the well established focus was effective in preventing secondary discharges; indeed it was found that the mirror focus was totally dependent on the integrity of inter-hemispheric fibres. In conjunction with these studies biochemical and also pharmacological studies were made. The former included studies of RNA, DNA, and protein metabolism. These showed that contrary to the findings of Morrell, the development of cobalt-induced epilepsy was associated with changes in these substances. Neurochemical transmitter substances were also being studied. Focal epileptic discharges could be caused or could be facilitated by a lack of inhibitory transmitters, such as GABA, or a relative excess of an excitory substance, such as glutamate.

The pharmacological studies showed that certain anti-convulsants such as phenobarbitone, diphenylhydantoin, and ethosuximide did not prevent the development of mirror discharges.

Behavioural studies were also made, using an ultrasonic technique to provide a print-out of the activities of the animals' behaviour.

The conclusion was that the experimental model that was developed showed great promise as a tool for further investigations into some of the many problems of epilepsy (Ashcroft, Townsend, Dow, McQueen and Harris, 1973).

Full reports on the work of the MRC (Medical Research Council) Brain Metabolism Unit (MRC/BMU) are available in its publications.

Those of us in the Edinburgh MRC-BMU joined up with the consultant neurosurgeon Mr R. M. Kalbag and his staff in the Newcastle Neurosurgical Unit to study the possibility of preventing post-traumatic epilepsy. We took into account those head injury patients who appeared to have a high risk of developing epilepsy. The factors were one or more of:

- A post-traumatic period of amnesia (PTA) for more than 24 hours, that is, until the return of continuous memory.
- An intracranial haematoma.
- A persistent (significant) neurological deficit.
- Dural penetration.
- A depressed fracture of the skull.

A relatively low, indeed very low, incidence of post-traumatic epilepsy was found in our patients.

There was no proof that in this double-blind, randomised trial, there was any benefit regarding the prevention of epilepsy, in those who had the phenytoin. Thus the possible benefits of routine prescriptions of anticonvulsant drugs for patients with a severe head injury remained, and remains, uncertain. Our double-blind study was of 164 patients and lasted two years. Understandably, patient compliance was a problem. We decided to discontinue prescribing routinely for such patients a regime of anticonvulsant drugs, and the development of any seizure like symptoms remained very low.

Regarding possible indication for a neurosurgical operation for epilepsy; quite briefly, these aspects are taken into account:

1. Discovery of the likely pathology, such as a brain tumour, a cerebral arteriovenous anomaly (AVM) or a meningocerebral cicatrix (scar). Operative excision of these cannot guarantee abolition of the fits, but they may become easier to control with anticonvulsant drugs.
2. The clinical features of the epilepsy, in particular if the fits are in the form of temporal lobe epilepsy.

3. A complete failure of optimal medical anticonvulsant treatment.
4. Relevant EEG findings.
5. If the defined focus of the epilepsy is in a 'safe area' of the brain.
6. If the fits include significant intellectual and psychological aspects which are not being controlled by anticonvulsant medications.

The investigation and neurosurgical operative treatment of patients with intractable temporal lobe epilepsy (TLE) has been one of my main interests. Once the patient comes into the category of TLE, and has been thoroughly investigated, the main aspects of the operation are discussed with the patient in lay terms. Approval being obtained, the operation is carried out. There are two possibilities, either a temporal lobectomy or a stereotactic operation, usually aiming to diathermise the deep nucleus, the amygdaloid nucleus in the temporal lobe of the brain. With a lobectomy the pathologist may well discover a discrete abnormality, a hamartoma deep in the temporal lobe, to be the culprit for the fits. When cases are carefully selected the epilepsy can very often be abolished, or there will be far fewer fits.

Many people with epilepsy can have some practical problems with their day to day living. For a number of years I was the Chairman of the SE Scotland Region Society for Epilepsy. This society, and others like it in the UK, are voluntary bodies, giving advice and support to people with epilepsy, on many aspects of this common disorder.

Epilepsy can occur in animals, indeed I understand that it is seen in certain monkeys in captivity, and have been told that the cause appears to be related to diet. Lack of certain vitamins, possibly mainly vitamin B, may be a factor, and appropriate treatment is usually effective.

Familial bovine epilepsy and ataxia in Angus cattle

Some years ago I was involved in an unusual research project concerning numbers of Angus cattle, in the UK and elsewhere.

A request was made to the Medical Research Council (MRC) Brain Metabolism Unit in Edinburgh University in 1977, by Dr R. M. Barlow of the Animal Diseases Research Association, Morden Institute in Edinburgh, knowing that we were involved with basic scientific researches on various aspects of epilepsy. He told us about an unusual disease that was affecting many cross-bred Aberdeen Angus cattle. The disease was of real concern to the beef industry. The affected cattle had developed severe convulsions and became very ataxic. The condition had a fatal outcome.

We were asked if we could help in a practical way, to study this very serious illness involving Angus cattle. We agreed.

The first problem was to catch the diseased Angus cattle, and also normal Jersey cattle, as controls, in wet, muddy fields. There were five Angus cattle, and two Jersey ones.

The plan was to sample quantities of ventricular and cisterna magna cerebrospinal fluid (CSF) for a study of the chemistry, and also to carry out electrocorticography to study the 'brain waves'. Apparently no such procedures had previously been carried out in such animals.

Under a general anaesthetic, each operation lasted from 4½ up to 6½ hours. The skulls and brains of the animals are of course very different from those of humans, but the lateral ventricles and the cisterna magna were cannulated, and fine catheters were inserted and were attached to Rickham type reservoirs, for later sampling of CSF. Then three types of electrodes were placed over the dura (the outer membrane covering the brain), in the frontal and occipital regions of the brain, for later electroencephalography studies. Post-operative recoveries were normal.

The CSF and the EEG findings were interesting. Details of these and of the operative procedures are given in the publication of Barlow, Dow, and Harris, 1978. Neuropathology studies of the brains from the diseased Angus cattle showed swelling and vacuolation of the Purkinje cells of the cerebellum. These cells are important concerning neuro-humeral trans-mission in the central nervous system. The brains of the control animals showed no neuropathological changes. The disease was subsequently dealt with by selective out-breeding.

Many of the aspects of the symptom-complex of epilepsy were given in greater detail and with several additional items, and with tables, figures, charts and photographs, also with full references in *The Hans Berger Centenary Symposium on Epilepsy* which took place in Edinburgh in July 1973, in the University of Edinburgh and the Royal College of Surgeons of Edinburgh.

I felt that it would be important and appropriate to commemorate the 100th anniversary of the birth of Dr Hans Berger, to celebrate the unique pioneering work of this psychophysiologist, who in 1924 discovered the electrical activity of the human brain. He introduced the term 'electro-encephalography', subsequently abbreviated to 'EEG'. His initial studies were carried out on his own children.

Berger was an intellectual, somewhat shy, reticent man. His first observations were published in 1929 in a not well known medical journal.

But two distinguished British doctors, Lord Adrian and Dr B. H. C. Matthews, had heard Berger give a lecture on the EEG at a small German medical meeting, and recognised the great importance of Berger's work, and they had the lecture published in Britain and elsewhere, bringing Berger almost immediate international recognition.

He did not accept Nazi ideology, and was eventually ousted from the academic scene, but he became known as 'the Father of Electroencephalography' in recognition of his scientific contributions. However he was a lonely man, struggling against great odds which eventually overwhelmed him. He became depressed, and took his own life in 1941, aged sixty-eight years.

My plan and hope was to have an international symposium in Edinburgh, on the present status and thinking on the several aspects of epilepsy by attracting distinguished scientists from all over the world to participate in an authoritative, up to date symposium. Twenty-five countries were represented. Participants included: A. Carlsson, J. K. Merlis, R. G. Hill, J. E. Walker, A. Angel, B. S. Meldrum, B. Cavazzo, G. W. Ashcroft, P. Harris, K. Sano, D. M. Woodbury, J. Donaldson, J. C. Gilbert, C. B. Gardner, J. A. N. Corsellis, F. Plum, C. Ounsted, M. C. Batison, P. A. Toseland, C. Serra, A. Richens, C. Christiansen, E. H. Reynolds, R. Vizioli, B. Ramamurthi, K. Vaernet, T. Rasmussen, F. J. Gillingham, A. A. Donaldson, V. M. Cairns, N. M. Dott, K. Sourek, J. H. Hutchison, M. J. Parsonage, R. L. McLaurin, J. Laidlaw, D. Sumner, A. Heinonen, T. A. Betts, and P. Gloor.

As Chairman of the Epilepsy Society of Edinburgh and South East Region, and a member of the Medical Research Council (MRC) Brain Metabolism Unit, associations were made with the International Bureau for Epilepsy; the International League Against Epilepsy (British Branch); the British Epilepsy Association; the Scottish Home and Health Department; and the Scottish Epilepsy Association. The symposium took place from 1 to 5 July 1973. The proceedings were edited, and the volume was published (Harris and Mawdsley, 1974). I chaired the Symposium, which took place in the University of Edinburgh, under these four sections:

1. Basic Aspects of Epilepsy and its Treatment.
2. Natural History and Management of Epilepsy.
3. Surgical Aspects of Epilepsy.
4. Epilepsy and the Community.

Closing Addresses:

(a) The Natural History and Management of Epilepsy. Professor A. Earl
     Walker, John Hopkins University, USA.
(b) Summing Up. Dr C. Ousted, Park Hospital for Children, Oxford.
(c) The Last Word. Dr Denis Williams, The National Hospital, Queen
     Square, London.
(d) Hans Berger Centenary Oration. Psychophysiology and the Discovery
     of the Human Electroencephalogram. Professor Pierre Gloor, Mon-
     treal, Canada.

Dr Wilder Penfield, OM

In Montreal, Canada, we were the guests of Dr and Mrs Wilder Penfield.
They were wonderful hosts. He was a distinguished neurosurgeon, with a
superb comprehensive department, first rate staff and a large number of
trainees. Britain awarded him the high honour of the OM (the Order of
Merit). One day I watched him from the viewing gallery in the operating
theatre carrying out what was possibly his last of many temporal
lobectomies for a patient with severe, intractable epilepsy. Most
interesting!

Stereotactic neurosurgery

To reach a particular deep part of the brain for the treatment of a patient
or to take a biopsy, special measures are necessary, to arrive at that part with
minimal operative interference and with extreme accuracy.

Thus came the development of stereotactic neurosurgery: *stereo* (Greek –
three dimensional) and *tangere* (Latin – to touch).

Stereotactic surgery is probably based on the proclamation of the French
philosopher, Rene Descartes: '*Cogito ergo sum*' – I think, therefore I am. He
apparently observed the three co-ordinates necessary to pin-point something in space (or in the brain). Subsequently, some centuries later Sir
Victor Horsley and Robert Clarke devised a special 'stereotactic apparatus',
using it in 1906 for laboratory animal work. It is necessary to have three
co-ordinates to reach a pre-determined point in a sphere, or indeed
neurologically, in a human brain. Several important developments followed, and in 1947 Spiegel and Wycis in the USA modified the
Horsley-Clarke apparatus and began to do human stereotactic brain
operations. Human brain atlases for such surgery became available. Contrast

radiological studies demonstrate certain deep vital parts in the brain, and a stereotactic frame is attached firmly to the patient's head through a small opening in the skull (a burr-hole) in the previously determined site. Local anaesthetic is used for a small scalp incision, then, using a special drill a hole (burr) is made down to the dura. The hole will be about ¾ inch (20 mm) in diameter. A fine instrument is passed through a tube in the frame, to reach the previously defined deep part of the brain. The instrument can be an electrode to permit controlled destruction, for example with coagulation diathermy, or a fine special needle to permit biopsies of the brain.

The procedure is invariably carried out under local anaesthesia (the bone and the brain have no sensation) to see and study the clinical effects, and to obtain the co-operation of the patient. Also, electroneurophysiological studies can be made. The procedure is an elegant one, and has several applications in neurosurgery, including:

1. Functional neurosurgery for (a) Parkinson's disease, (b) certain other movement disorders, (c) certain intractable pain conditions, (d) certain highly selected psychiatric conditions.
2. Fine needle biopsy of brain tumours and cysts.
3. For certain, highly selected patients with intractable epilepsy, in particular temporal lobe epilepsy.

In our department John Gillingham, having spent time working with Guiot in Paris, about 1955, introduced the procedure of stereotactic cerebral surgery. Others including myself took it up. John also pursued interesting and important researches with the procedure.

One of the most dramatic experiences in neurosurgery is to witness the immediate clinical effects on a patient with Parkinson's disease when the tip of the introduced special probe reaches the precise region deep in the brain during the operation. A particular case comes to mind: the operation took place in the operating theatre of Ward 20, Royal Infirmary of Edinburgh, overlooking Heriots School and Edinburgh Castle. The patient lay on his back on the operating table, fully conscious and co-operative. The stereotactic frame had been secured to his head; his right arm was vigorously shaking in the typical Parkinson manner, and his right arm and leg were typically 'cog-wheel' spastic. These signs had been present for years, not responding to medications. When the special probe was carefully inserted into the appropriate part of the stereotactic frame and passed deeply into the patient's brain to reach the pre-determined target point in the basal ganglia, deeply situated complex, neural structures in the brain, there was immediate cessation of the awful arm tremor – a most remarkable thing to witness, and there was also abolition of the spasticity (increased tone) in his right arm and leg: wonderful! Next the 'mechanical lesion' made by the probe/electrode, required, as is usual in this operation, to be made permanent, using electro-coagulation. My practice was for the theatre sister to count down: 5, 4, 3, 2, 1 seconds (of electro-coagulation), but on reaching 'one', the one o'clock gun in Edinburgh Castle went off, and the patient gave a jump; happily the frame was securely attached to his head. I explained what had happened, and indeed, all was well!

Stereotactic neurosurgery was obviously an important new procedure in neurosurgery, and I visited and studied various techniques, including a variety of stereotactic apparatuses, in a number of neurosurgical centres, including New York (Dr Irving Cooper) and Dr Petter Lindstrom (Salt Lake City, Utah). Dr Cooper was an important early pioneer. Dr Lindstrom devised a new procedure using stereotaxy and a high frequency high intensity sound, treating selected patients who had intractable pain, and some with intractable psychiatric disorders. He had found that brain cells were apparently much more susceptible to his method of selectively destroying very small defined deep regions of the brain, apparently sparing cerebral fibres, while also the cerebral blood supply remained intact. Dr Lindstrom was an excellent host. His wife had been the famous film star Ingrid Bergman. We borrowed the car of their daughter, Pia.

Included amongst several distinguished neurosurgical visitors to our department was the celebrated Dr Henry Wycis.

Altered states of awareness

There are certain serious clinical neurological states in which a patient has a significant altered state of awareness. Such states are important for all concerned: patients, doctors, nurses and paramedical personnel, and the relatives. The patient is very ill, and expert hospital management is essential. Neurosurgeons play an important role in the management.

Non-medical people will most likely not be familiar with some aspects of these severe illnesses, thus a brief note on them could be appropriate. Therefore I suggest that they may wish to seek help and explanations from a medical doctor.

(1) Coma

Coma is a state of loss of consciousness and of awareness of self and of the environment. The patient lies with eyes closed, with no understandable response to external stimuli, or of inner needs. That is, a state of unrousable unresponsiveness. There are many possible causes for the development of coma, usually severe brain damage from injury or disease.

(2) The persistent vegetative state (PVS)

The patient is in a state of wakefulness, being awake, but not aware, without cognitive functions or the ability to appreciate or respond. He is devoid of intellectual activity and is speechless. The eyes may open but do not track and explore the surroundings. There are no purposeful limb movements to painful stimuli. Respirations and cardiac and gastro-intestinal actions are normal. The patient is wholly dependent on others for care and was probably comatose to begin with. As with coma, the pathology is usually of serious brain damage from trauma; the commonest non-traumatic cause is cardio-pulmonary arrest from certain diseases or drugs, or sometimes in relation to a general anaesthetic.

The term 'vegetative' is used because only vegetative or autonomic functions are preserved. The brainstem recovers function, but the cerebral hemispheres cannot recover. Thus there is no higher mental activity. The patient is kept alive by resuscitative measures, and requires nourishment and fluids, and the prevention of respiratory infections and cutaneous pressure ulcers.

There are no laboratory means to diagnose the PVS, and reliance is on the trend of the patient's clinical state. If the symptoms continue for a long time – for two or more weeks – a decision will require to be made regarding the withdrawal of artificial feeding and of fluids. (The term 'PVS' was coined by Plum and Jennett in 1972.)

In August 1995 I was asked if I could please agree to examine and give my opinion on a patient in a Scottish hospital who appeared to be in a PV state, as the outcome would be decided in a Court of Law. The case was fully reported in the British media. The patient was a fifty-year-old lady. She had severe brain anoxia (lack of oxygen), possibly from a viral infection of the brain. She showed all the clinical features of the PVS, and had been like this for over three years. Careful assessment and examination of the patient, studying all of the medical and nursing records and viewing the radiological studies, I came to the same conclusion as a consultant neurologist, who had also been called in to report on the woman.

The husband and close relatives expressed a strong desire for cessation of food and fluids; they had visited her regularly, during the three years. Their strong desire was that she should be allowed to die in peace and with dignity. However, the Hospital Trust took the action, technically against the immediate family. There was a legal move to protect the family from possible prosecution, if and when food and fluids were discontinued. The case came to court, a Civil Court in the Court of Session in Edinburgh, but to protect the medical doctors from possible prosecution, the case was then transferred to the Criminal Court.

The outcome was that the relatives succeeded with their serious, determined wishes regarding the course of action they wished for the patient, and death occurred.

(3) The locked-in-syndrome (LIS)

The locked-in syndrome (LIS) is a serious clinical neurological state which can be considered to result from a vascular or traumatic lesion of the ventral (anterior) part of the vital region of the brain, the brainstem, indeed the part of the latter called the pons.

Clinically, the patient is fully alert, but without the ability to respond to external stimuli. There is tetraplegia (paralysis of all four limbs) and the patient is unable to speak. Vertical eye movements are retained and he can only communicate through blinking. The cough reflex is impaired, so there is a risk of the aspiration of saliva, etc., and this can lead to pneumonia. There is bilateral facio-glosso-pharyngeal-laryngeal palsy; that is, paralysis of facial muscles, the tongue, pharynx and larynx.

Such patients understandably present a tremendous challenge to doctors, nurses and physiotherapists for their management. Over many months there can be some partial recovery of motor functions, beginning in the hands and toes.

(4) Brain death

Previously, the diagnosis of death was made when there was cardiac failure and arrest. Resuscitative measures had probably been taken: cardio-pulmonary resuscitation (CPR), with assisted ventilation, using a ventilator. It may be possible to prolong life in this way, and with appropriate food and fluids.

Since 1976, the state of Brain Death has been accepted as death of the individual, with loss of function of the cerebral hemispheres and of the brainstem. (There may be some spinal reflex activity.) There is coma. The patient is unresponsive to deep painful stimuli. The pupils are dilated and fixed, and do not react to light. The corneal, gag and cough reflexes are absent. Doll's eye testing and vestibular cold caloric stimulation give no response regarding eye movements. There is no spontaneous breathing, and a respirator is required. Apnoea (loss of ability to breathe) is tested by disconnecting the respirator, to allow the PCO2 (carbon dioxide) to rise to 60mm of mercury; if there is no response, the patient is in the state of 'brain death'. The usual procedure is to examine the patient clinically on two separate occasions, by two separate, senior doctors who are not involved in the patient's management, six hours apart, to permit the definite diagnosis of brain death.

Some patients in this state of brain death can be suitable donors for organ transplants.

It is stressed that initially, it must be ascertained that the patient is not on a large dose of hypnotic drugs that may depress respirations; and also ensure that the patient is not hypothermic.

CHAPTER 3

The spine

Opportunity to learn walks into the operating room with any surgeon who
has unanswered questions in mind.

Wilder Penfield

Degenerative diseases

Lumbar spondylosis

Aᶠᵗᵉʳ ᴀ ᴅᴀʏ's ᴏᴘᴇʀᴀᴛɪɴɢ, I returned to my office. The cleaners had left
a pile of X-rays on the floor. I bent down to lift them up, and was
turning round to place them back on my desk when I experienced sudden
acute pain from my back, shooting down the front of my right thigh, to
the knee. The diagnosis was obvious, but I wanted an independent check,
and immediately contacted a consultant medical neurology colleague, who
indeed confirmed that I most likely had a rupture of the lumbar 3–4
intervertebral disc on the right side, implicating the right L4 nerve root.

My back muscles were in spasm, and back movements were severely
restricted. The right femoral nerve stretch test was positive. There were
fasciculations of the right quadriceps muscle group, and the right knee jerk
was absent. There was depressed cutaneous sensation in the right L4
dermatome. Surprisingly the pain disappeared; to me this was bad, and
made urgent surgical treatment even more necessary, as I reckoned that the
damaged right L4 nerve root was so damaged as to be unable to transmit
pain sensation to my brain.

A consultant neurosurgical colleague was contacted. He agreed with the
diagnosis, and a necessary imaging study was done, showing the abnormal
L3/4 disc impinging on the right L4 nerve root.

At operation, all was revealed. There was a large extrusion and
sequestration of the L3/4 intervertebral disc, severely compressing the right
L4 nerve root. The disc material was excised, completely decompressing
the taut nerve root.

The result was excellent with no neurological abnormalities, including
absence of pain.

The term in general use for degenerative disease of the spine is
spondylosis (*spondyle* – pertaining to the joints of the spine). The condition

62

is as old as man himself. Everyone over the age of seventy years will have obvious spondylosis, but not of actual clinical significance. Lumbar spondylosis is probably the commonest condition treated by neurosurgeons.

An intervertebral disc consists of a central, semi-fluid part, the nucleus pulposus, surrounded by a ring of strong, elastic fibres, the annulus fibrosus; and on each side there are facet joints, which articulate with the facets above and below the adjacent vertebrae. Spondylosis is mainly seen in the lower lumbar spinal region; also in the mid and lower parts of the cervical spine, and in the latter region, bony osteophytes (excrescences) develop along the edges of the vertebral bodies. The pressure within a disc changes with age, and certainly increases with sudden flexion and rotation of the trunk, or/and lifting something or someone heavy. The annulus undergoes degenerative changes and the nucleus pulposus then protrudes in the lumbar spine, postero-laterally, impinging on the adjacent spinal nerve. There are also arthritic changes in the facet joints. All of this is the setting for the protrusion (discs do not slip) of a disc, usually resulting in a characteristic clinical syndrome ('*syndrome*' – a concurrence of several symptoms and signs in a disease; '*symptoms*' – those perceived by the patient; '*signs*' – what is found on clinical, 'hands on' examination of the patient).

Clinical features include low back pain with radiation of pain into a particular aspect of a lower limb (occasionally into both lower limbs), in a spinal nerve root distribution. This is called radicular pain (or radiculopathy). The discs most commonly involved by a disc protrusion are L4–5 and L5–S1 (L = lumbar vertebra; S = sacral vertebra). Less commonly, L3–4, usually in an older person, are involved. Thus, respectively the nerve roots implicated are L5, S1 and L4. There is limitation of spinal flexion. In the straight left raising test (flexion at the hip, leg elevated with the knee unbent) the leg must be raised to a right angle because the pains are made worse, and more so with flexion of the foot. There will most likely be appropriate motor (weakness of leg muscles), sensory (depressed skin sensation) and reflex (knee and ankle) changes.

Occasionally an acute, very serious 'disc syndrome' occurs, due to a sudden, massive protrusion – indeed extrusion, of an L4–5, or L5–S1 disc, compressing the cauda equina nerve roots, and causing severe pain in the back and legs, weakness of the legs, and a degree of paralysis of urinary bladder, bowel and sexual functions. Urgent neurosurgical treatment is required to excise the offending disc and decompress the nerves. It is noted that in adults, the spinal cord ends in the upper lumbar region, and beyond this, the lumbar and sacral nerves pass down to reach their exit foramina (openings) in the spine. The appearance of these nerves, together, is called the cauda equina (horse's tail).

With acute, severe nerve root compression the initial pain may disappear, because the nerve can no longer transmit pain sensation (as happened to myself).

Investigations. These can be through imaging studies: plain X-rays, and MRI. (Previously, before 'scans' became available, contrast X-rays using radio-opaque Myodil were carried out.)

Differential diagnosis. Classically, with a history of back pain from strain or a definite torsion, flexion injury, with lumbar backache and leg pain, the cause is a protruded intevertebral disc; that is, back and leg pain. Possibly, and rarely, there could be a different pathology, a spinal neoplasm, primary or secondary.

Indications for operative treatment

Briefly these are:

1. A massive disc protrusion causing a cauda equina syndrome.
2. Definite signs of neurological involvement in a leg; with motor, sensory, and sometimes, reflex changes (knee and ankle jerks).
3. Poor response to 'good' non-operative management (rest, initially in bed; simple oral analgesics, anti-inflammatory non steroid drugs limitation of arduous work, domestic and play activities. Treatment will include physiotherapy.
4. Recurrent attacks of back and leg pain, not responding to good non-operative treatment, including complete, strict bed rest for 2–3 weeks.

Operative treatment. Excision of the protruding intevertebral disc. Mobilisation from the first post-operation day is advisable, with physiotherapy.

A different backache disorder

I had developed another back problem, but it had the clinical features of a lumbar facet joint disorder. The pains involved my lower back and extended into the left buttock. They were getting worse and, importantly, were aggravated by back extension. I had been interested in the nerve supply of the facet joints, and had carried out dissections in the Edinburgh University Department of Anatomy, staining the delicate nerves and tracing them as they reached the facet joints, and had become familiar with facet joint disorders. I arranged to be seen by my consultant anaesthetic colleague, Dr Murray Carmichael, who was also in charge of a Pain Clinic in the Western General Hospital. He examined me, and offered to treat me. I readily agreed. Under X-ray control he injected the affected lumbar facet joints with a local anaesthetic followed by a steroid. The result was 'magic' – complete, and indeed, I may say, with permanent abolition of the awful pain. I was very thankful.

Acute LBP, without necessarily radicular pain, can result from several diseases and injuries, including trauma, also from an acute epidural haematoma (bleeding causing a blood clot), an acute epidural spinal abscess, and also some rarer causes. Back strains at work or play can cause spasm of the back muscles and also have dynamic physical effects on the joints and ligaments of the lumbar spinal region. LBP is a very common condition indeed, with a multiplicity of causes; the great majority of such patients do not have a more serious condition such as a neoplasm, but consideration must be given to the possibility of an inflammatory cause – the myopathies – or to lumbar spine stenosis, or from spondylolisthesis. Patients with acute LBP can require the services of their general practitioner, and often a physiotherapist. Depending on the whole syndrome, referral to a rheumatologist or an orthopaedic surgeon may be required.

My continuing interest in the subject of LBP was recently re-awakened in me when my daughter, a physiotherapist, drew my attention to two interesting and important scientific articles:

(1) 'Acute low back pain: a new paradigm for management', an editorial in the British Medical Journal (BMJ) 1996: 313: 1344 (30 November). New, important and quite different guidelines in management were issued by the Royal College of General Practitioners and these are described, and are in agreement with the American Agency for Health Care Policy guidelines. The habit of bed rest and 'taking it easy', is replaced by a rapid return to normal activities. Imaging (including radiology) and specialist referral are deemed unnecessary. Psychosocial factors should be considered. Bed rest is not recommended; patients should stay as active as possible, and continue normal daily activities. Drugs should be prescribed at regular intervals, not as required, beginning with paracetamol and non-steroidal anti-inflammatory drugs. Spinal manipulation may be considered for relief of symptoms within six weeks of onset. Patients who have not returned to ordinary activities and work by six weeks should be referred for an exercise programme.

(2) *Clinical Guidelines for the Management of Acute Low Back Pain*, February 1999. This is an excellent article; contributing organisations are the Royal College of General Practitioners, the Chartered Society of Physiotherapy, the British Orthopaedic Association, the British Chiropractic Association and the National Back Association. Readers are referred to the Royal College of General Practitioners, 14 Princes Gate, Hyde Park, London SW7 1PU. A patient booklet is also available: *The Back Book*, published by the Stationery Office (ISBN 011 702 0788).

It is noted that these two articles most probably relate to acute, severe low lumbar strains and stresses (which I think used to be called 'lumbago'), but which are disabling and miserable for the patient.

Cervical spondylosis

Like lumbar spondylosis, cervical spondylosis (CS) is very common ('*cervix*' – neck), being frequently seen as an incidental finding in imaging studies (plain X-rays, and scans) of the neck of people taken for some other disorder. It is seen in some 75 per cent of people over the age of fifty years, especially males, and in all people over the age of seventy years. People with CS may develop neurological symptoms and signs, often as a result of minor, possibly repetitive trauma, causing sudden to and fro movements of the neck. Less often, it can result from a more severe neck injury, which would include the so called 'whiplash injury', inside a vehicle, with sudden acute neck movements. Degenerative changes occur in both the nucleus pulposus, and the annular fibrosus parts of a disc, but usually more than one cervical disc is affected. The annulus gives way, and there is a disc protrusion. Physical stresses occur and osteophytes are found at the edges of vertebral bodies. The osteophytes are outgrowths of the bone, and are commonly seen in CS, whereas they are less common in lumbar spondylosis.

Posterior bulging of cervical discs will mechanically compress the spinal cord, or the cervical nerve roots, or both cord and roots. There will also be vascular (blood vessel) compression, causing a degree of ischaemia (reduction of blood supply) to the spinal cord. The commonest level for a cervical disc protrusion is C5/6 (the disc between the 5th and 6th cervical vertebrae, written as C5/6); next are C4/5 and C6/7. Very occasionally there is an acute rupture of a cervical disc with immediate very serious effects of cord damage, resulting in a degree of tetraparesis (partial paralysis and sensory loss, and paralysis of bladder and bowel and sexual functions).

This is an urgent situation, requiring immediate admission to a Neuro-surgical Department for investigations and treatment.

Clinical presentations

- A radicular (nerve root) syndrome ('*radix*' – a root), with neck pain and stiffness, and arm pain (occasionally, both arms). In more severe cases, there is also disturbance of neurological functions in the arm(s); motor weakness, sensory changes – disturbance of skin (cutaneous) sensation, numbness, tingling; depression or loss of the arm deep reflexes (at the elbows and wrists).
- A myelopathic syndrome ('*myelo*' – the spinal cord). There is usually a long history of progressive spinal cord involvement, with weakness of the legs, more so than of the arms. There is a stiff, clumsy spastic gait. There is usually no neck pain, but the patient has a stiff neck. There are variable sensory changes but no disturbance of urinary bladder or bowel or sexual functions. If there is a long delay of one, and certainly two or more years, in recognising the condition, the patient will become increasingly paralysed, and operative treatment may not then be very effective. Cervical spondylotic myelopathy is probably the commonest cause of disturbance of spinal cord function seen in Western countries.
- A combination of a radicular and a myelopathic syndrome. I have recognised these myelopathic syndromes occurring in cervical spondylo-sis; relating to the anatomical location in the cervical spinal cord.
- Anterior spinal cord. Paralysis of the body below (distal to) the clinical and imaging studies level. The sensations of touch, position and vibration are preserved and bladder functions normal.
- Lateral spinal cord. A Brown-Sequard syndrome. One lateral half of the spinal cord is involved, with ipsilateral paresis (partial paralysis), and loss of joint sensation below the level of the cord lesion; and contralateral loss of pain and temperature sensation (the spino-thalamic tracts nerve fibres) in the cord cross-over to the opposite side of the cord as they pass upwards to the part of the brain called the thalamus, and from there, to the sensory cortex area of the brain, to reach consciousness.
- Central spinal cord. There is disproportionally greater motor impairment (paralysis) of the arms than the legs. Sensory loss is variable. Urinary bladder function may be affected.
- Posterior spinal cord. Neck pain, and pain and tingling and increased skin

sensation (hyperaesthesia) in the arms, and sometimes also in the trunk. There is minimal motor (muscle power) involvement.

• Subtotal cord (SC). A mixture of the above.

Investigations

These include plain X-rays of the cervical spine, including movement studies; and lateral views in flexion and extension to assess stability. Other imaging studies (in previous times, Myodil, a radio-opaque fluid) – a myelogram (see figure 37). Subsequently came the MRI (magnetic resonance imaging).

Treatment

Patients with a radicular (cervical nerve root) syndrome usually respond well to simple measures. They should limit arduous activities, especially those involving much neck flexion. Simple oral analgesics or a non-steroid anti-inflammatory drug are given. Physiotherapy is very helpful. Some patients require a collar, but not a soft (felt) one. I prefer the Philadelphia rigid collar. They may require bed rest, preferably lying on a foam-plastic head and neck support (Harris 1966). I do not favour neck manipulation as it can be dangerous and cause a serious increase in neurological damage. If after about three weeks the condition has not resolved, and certainly if there is more than neck pain and stiffness and arm pain, but there are also definite motor (loss of power), sensory changes and reduction of the arm deep reflexes, the patient should be recommended for early referral to a neurosurgeon for further investigations and most likely for operative treatment.

All patients with cervical spondylotic myelopathy must be considered for operative treatment. The evolution of the operative treatment is important and interesting. For many years, a laminectomy (posterior) procedure was used, but the anterior aspect of the cervical spine was being mechanically compressed by degenerate intervertebral disc(s) and osteophytes, and often also the blood supply to the cord was compromised. Even slight retraction of an already damaged spinal cord was fraught with the danger of real neural damage, sometimes with catastrophic major spinal paralysis, when attempting to reach and remove the degenerate disc and the osteophytes. Unlike the large diameter of the lumbar spinal canal where there is no spinal cord but there are nerve roots, there is little room in the cervical region of the spine (Harris 1960).

A more anatomical operative approach was desirable, and I was already familiar with this to remove protruded thoracic intervertebral discs, by a trans-thoracic (through the chest) procedure. (A patient I operated on for this pathology is mentioned elsewhere in this book, when I excised a thoracic disc protrusion by a laminectomy (posterior) operation. This was many years ago, before I approached such lesions trans-thoracically.) We were also operating on patients with spinal cord involvement from tuberculosis (Pott's paraplegia) by an antero-lateral, trans-thoracic approach, to excise the tuberculous material and evacuate the tuberculous abscess. Like a number of surgeons, I disliked the posterior laminectomy operation to treat cervical spondylotic myelopathy. I visited the John Hopkin's Hospital and Medical School, spent time with Drs Smith and Robinson, and watched them do an antero-lateral operation for cervical spondylosis which had caused a radicular syndrome. Apparently, the whole of the diseased disc was not excised, nor were all of the osteophytes. They inserted a bone graft between the vertebral bodies, to discourage the formation of further osteophytes. The patient's pain was relieved. Follow-up was one year (Smith and Robinson 1955).

Wiltberger (1953) invented surgical instruments to enable him to carry out an inter-vertebral body fusion, after excising a protruded lumbar intervertebral disc, and Cloward (1958) studied Wiltberger's work, and had the instruments that he used for lumbar spine fusion (drilling holes and the insertion of a dowel of iliac bone) modified, and used them for an anterior operative approach to the cervical spine for patients with a ruptured cervical disc, causing a radicular syndrome.

On my return to Edinburgh I had further modifications of the Wiltberger-Cloward surgical instruments made for me, and initially carried out some studies in the Edinburgh University Department of Anatomy. I then chose what appeared to be suitable patients with neurological disturbances from cervical spondylosis, some with a radicular syndrome, most with varying degrees and types of myelopathy. I reported on my first 117 patients (Harris 1968), with a follow-up study of up to 6½ years. I operated on many more patients; at times, two or sometimes three in a week. Quite often it was necessary to operate on two, three and occasionally four levels in the cervical spine. Quite briefly, the anterior operation consists of making a small skin incision on the right antero-lateral aspect of the neck. Dissection is carried down to the front (anterior aspect) of the cervical spine. The precise cervical spine anatomical level is ascertained, and then, using the special instruments a half inch diameter hole is very carefully drilled through the centre of the affected disc and adjacent aspects of the vertebral bodies above and below. The posterior common ligament of the spine is now seen, and a thorough excision of any remaining osteophytes and degenerate disc is carried out. A dowel of bone taken from the patient's iliac crest (the dowel is shaped like a cork) is inserted into the drilled hole and gently tapped into place. Post-operative care is routine. The patient is allowed up from the first post-operative day. I would stress the importance of taking special care when a patient with cervical spondylosis (with or without neurological changes) is being intubated for an anaesthetic, as great care is necessary when the head and neck are extended for the intubation of the airway. The same holds good for patients with a suspected or known cervical spine injury; simply lifting the head and neck up to place an X-ray plate under the head can cause very severe cervical spinal cord damage.

It appeared to me that, overall, patients with cervical spondylosis causing a radicular syndrome, and also those with anterior spinal cord myelopathy and those with a lateral cord syndrome, usually do very well with an anterior spinal operation. Those with a central or a posterior spinal cord syndrome however often have limited neurological improvement, but it is hoped that the progression of the cervical myelopathy would be halted.

I also designed and had special surgical instruments made for me to enable me to surgically approach the uppermost cervical vertebrae: C1 – the atlas, C2 – the axis, and the third (C3) cervical vertebra. This was for trans-oral (through the mouth) operative approaches, opening up the back of the pharynx to deal with pathological lesions, at the uppermost part of the cervical spine. The lesions include traumatic fractures, neoplasms, and infections.

Neoplasms

Neoplasms are either primary or secondary The secondary ones are usually metastatic, arising from a malignant tumour elsewhere in the body.

(1) Primary, intradural, extramedullary neoplasms

These develop within the dural covering of the spinal cord, and outwith the actual spinal cord. There are two types: meningiomas, arising from the dura and arachnoid (the coverings of the spinal cord); and schwannomas (neurofibromas), which arise from the coverings of the spinal nerves. These growths make up about 45 per cent of all spinal tumours. They are benign.

Spinal neural compression occurs, causing a degree of paraparesis: that is, disturbances of motor, sensory and urinary bladder function distal to the level of the growth. Especially with schwannomas, prominent pain in the distribution of the involved spinal nerve is a common symptom. As for all spinal neoplasms, special imaging studies by a radiologist are required. Treatment is straightforward, neurosurgical excision of the tumour; the results are usually excellent.

(2) Primary intradural, intramedullary ('medulla' – the spinal cord) neoplasms

These are rare, making up less than 5 per cent of spinal neoplasms. They occur within the spinal cord. The ependymomas are commoner than the astrocytomas – they can develop in children. Pain is not usually a symptom, but there is a progressive paraparesis. The ependymomas can very often be completely excised at operation, with meticulous microneurosurgery, working inside the quite small diameter of the spinal cord. Astrocytomas are more difficult to treat as there is no clear distinction between the tumour and the spinal cord which is being infiltrated. Additional radio-therapy can sometimes help.

(3) Secondary, extradural neoplasms

These are usually metastatic from a primary malignant tumour elsewhere in the body, such as the kidney, breast, lung or prostate. The vertebral column is invaded, with compression of the spinal cord and nerve roots. The history is usually short, and severe pain from bone invasion and nerve root involvement is common, with a rapidly developing paraparesis (that is, incomplete paraplegia). Clinical and imaging studies usually reveal the primary malignant growth. A decision is made by the neurosurgeon and the oncologist for the best treatment for the patient, but unfortunately, the prognosis is poor.

Infections

An acute epidural (extradural) abscess

This causes extremely severe spinal pain at the level of the infection, and exquisite tenderness, spinal cord compression and the general features of an acute infection. The condition must be considered and diagnosed urgently as the abscess must be surgically drained openly and the infection vigorously treated. Otherwise serious thrombophlebitis and arteritis will develop with infarction of the spinal cord, and with no recovery of neurological functions.

Tuberculosis of the spine

This is most likely one of the commonest causes of paraplegia in developing countries, especially with the addition of AIDS. It demands urgent medical, and if there is spinal cord involvement (called Pott's paraplegia), also neurosurgical treatment by medical and surgical doctors and associates familiar with the disease. Much can be achieved nowadays.

Congenital spine disorders

Congenital disorders of the spine are common. They are due to defective closure of the neural tube at its lower (caudal) end, with resultant neurological abnormalities, varying in severity and importance from (1) simple spina bifida occulta – just a skin dimple and an area of hairy skin, with no clinical importance. (2) A simple meningocele: a cystic-like deformity containing cerebrospinal fluid. There are usually no neurological abnormalities. The sac should be excised and if not dangerously thin, one should wait until up to six months to do this. (3) Meningo-myelocele. The sac contains CSF and spinal nerve roots, and there are significant neurological abnormalities, amounting to paraplegia, and hydrocephalus is usually also present. The condition requires expert medical and surgical treatment and continuing long term expert management is essential.

Other spinal disorders

Traumatic spinal cord injuries (TSCI) have received most worldwide interest, especially during and subsequent to World War II, with the development of special spinal units and departments in many countries, and the term 'SCI' is usually understood to be 'Traumatic SCI'. But the commonest causes by far, for spinal cord-nerve root lesions is not trauma, but a non-traumatic cause, including disorders and pathologies such as spinal tumours (neoplasms); spinal infections; multiple sclerosis (MS); anterior poliomyelitis (APM); the Guillain-Barre syndrome; venous malformations; severe vertebral column deformities such as kypho-sciolosis; non-traumatic extradural haematoma (a clot of blood) as may arise from certain blood disorders, during anti-coagulant treatment; haemophilia; and vascular malformation of the spinal cord, and intervertebral disc pathologies.

However, understandably once the diagnosis is made, appropriate treatment is given. If the patient has significant spinal cord-nerve root involvement, the same treatment as has already been described for traumatic SCI patients will be required, and some of these patients will be susceptible to the same complications and problems that can occur with patients who sustain a significant traumatic spinal cord injury.

Traumatic spinal cord injuries

Human traumatic spinal cord injuries (TSCI) have been recognised for over 4,000 years, as is known from the Egyptian papyri, translated in the Edwin Smith *Surgical Papyrus*. Patients with such injuries present real challenges for the doctors, and all of the other medical and other specialists involved in their care.

Prevention

A severe traumatic spinal cord injury (TSCI) is devastating for the individual. All reasonable measures must be taken to prevent such a catastrophe. The common causes are falls; vehicle accidents; sports accidents including contact sports, diving and skiing; and assaults, especially gunshot wounds. I instance the work of Professor Richard Schneider, my good friend, neurosurgeon, in Ann Arbor, Michigan, USA. He noted that some American football players developed a serious fracture of the cervical spine causing paraplegia or tetraplegia. He attended several games and had ciné photographs taken. The players had a helmet which came low down at the top of the back of their neck, and a strong metallic visor to protect the face. If an opposing player grabbed hold of the visor to push the player backwards, the lower part of the helmet could act as a fulcrum, hyper-extending the neck, which 'snaps' and he becomes tetraplegic. Appropriate measures were taken to prevent the occurrence of this devastating injury, by modifying the helmets.

The pre-Munro and Guttmann era

As the centuries and years have gone by, there was a gradual, better understanding of the many important aspects of TSCI. But even up to the time of World War I and indeed also for some years later, most people with a severe TSCI had a miserable life with a number of complications, and an early fatal outcome.

The modern, Munro and Guttmann era

There was a dramatic change in the understanding and in the management of people who had sustained a severe TSCI, when two distinguished doctors came on the scene; in the USA, Dr Donald Munro, and in the UK, Dr (later, Sir) Ludwig Guttmann.

Dr Donald Munro was a pupil of the famous neurosurgeon Frazier. Munro established a spinal centre in the Boston City Hospital in 1936, beginning with only ten beds. His 1943 publication heralded the modern treatment of patients with a severe TSCI. He was a man of ideas, erudite, an academic, a fine, caring physician, and a good administrator. He became known as 'The Father of Paraplegia'. He felt that the treatment of the vertebral column injury was of secondary importance to the neural aspects. He was against decompressive laminectomy; he had his patients turned two-hourly to prevent pressure sores, and invented and used a system called tidal drainage for the management of the paralysed urinary bladder. He was against the use of plaster of paris shells for his patients, was keen on excellent rehabilitation, and said that if a patient's arms were unaffected by their injury, the patient should eventually be able to be independent.

The other famous pioneer was Sir Ludwig Guttmann, a neurosurgeon trained by the distinguished German neurosurgeon Professor Otfried Foester in Breslau; Guttmann was his only pupil. Because of the fiendish Nazi atrocities, Guttmann, a Jew, required to leave Germany, and came to Oxford in England, where he continued his neurophysiological researches. Fortunately, he was 'discovered' by the eminent medical neurologist Brigadier George Riddoch, who subsequently found a niche for Guttmann in 1944 to establish a spinal injuries unit in Stoke Mandeville Hospital, in Aylesbury. This suited the determined, dynamic, demanding, enthusiastic Ludwig. He had had visits with Munro in Boston and they were good friends. The earlier patients admitted to Stoke Mandeville were nearly all young service people. Most came with horrific pressure skin ulcers, some extending to bone, and all were infected. Other complications of their TSCI (some had had multiple trauma) included badly infected urinary tracts, limb spasms and contractures, anaemia, poor nutrition, low morale and apathy and they were quite miserable. In Edinburgh in our Department of Surgical Neurology in the special war-time (EMS Emergency Medical

Services) in Bangour Hospital (near Edinburgh) we came across very similar, awful clinical problems. An extension of our Department as a war-time measure (to be 'temporary') was a spinal service for the longer term care of TSCI patients, in Edenhall Hospital in Musselburgh where there were resident surgical staff and attending staff; initially, Professor Norman Dott, neurosurgeon, Professor Sir Walter Mercer, orthopaedic surgeon, and Mr David Band, urological surgeon. Subsequently, Mr Douglas Lamb, orthopaedic surgeon, Mr Jack Newsam, urological surgeon, Mr Campbell Buchan, plastic surgeon, and myself were added. Many of the Munro and Guttmann medical measures were incorporated in the therapies for these young seriously injured service people.

I return to Guttmann, who became a close friend, staying in each other's homes, and I visited Stoke Mandeville on a number of occasions. He was a very caring doctor, an expert in the management of TSCI patients. He attracted dedicated medical, nursing, physiotherapy and occupational therapy staff to his unit. Strict orders were given and were duly carried out. These involved: two hourly, day and night, turning of patients to prevent cutaneous pressure sores; disallowing the use of plaster of paris shells; intermittent aseptic bladder catheterisetion, day and night; the expert surgical care of the awful pressure sores; conservative (non-operative) treatment for the injured spine; reduction of vertebral deformities by expert positioning of the patient; abhorring the use of metal plates and/or metal screws; full attention to the patient's psychological state and to vocational activities; introducing sporting involvements. He 'spread the gospel', and attracted many important visitors; he also started a new medical journal, *Paraplegia*; and pioneered the International Medical Society of Paraplegia (IMSOP).

Nowadays in the UK there are about three hundred new patients a year with a severe TSCI, mainly young males. It is said that about half of the patients have a cervical (of the neck) injury, and the majority of these have a complete lesion of the spinal cord, being tetraplegic or paraplegic. Thus there are relatively few new patients, many with significant multiple injuries, and each will have a different type and degree of TSCI. Understandably, even including TSCI patients from many countries, it is difficult to obtain matched controls to study the results of different types of patient management of the actual vertebral column injury.

The anatomical, physiological and biomedical aspects of TSCI are complex and require proper, practical knowledge and understanding. Furthermore, the quite frequent combination of associated injuries, for example, a cervical spinal injury and a head injury, can make the clinical situation extremely complex.

The initial management during the one to three hours are absolutely vital for the patient, as so much could go wrong, and remediable vertebral column-spinal cord and nerve root changes could be missed, or the diagnosis could be badly delayed, or, most unfortunately, the handling of the patient could be wrong, dangerous and unsatisfactory. Be suspicious of a TSCI, handle with great care, ensure a free airway. Ambulance personnel and paramedics play an important part. Keep careful records. Transport by the quickest, best, safest means preferably to a spinal injury service, part of a really good general hospital. I have come across tragedies where a patient with 'a possible neck injury' was being X-rayed in a hospital, and his head was gently lifted up to allow the X-ray plate to be put in place, when the patient suddenly became tetraplegic permanently.

Decisions are now taken concerning special, optimal management, including the best possible treatment for the injured vertebral column and the neural elements. Some controversy remains concerning the advisability/ necessity for surgical measures; that is, compared to 'conservative' (non-surgical) treatment. Decisions include the management of an 'unstable' fracture/dislocation; also for the urgent treatment of a traumatic intervertebral disc protrusion compressing the spinal cord.

Over the decades, a remarkable variety of types of metallic fixations and screws have been invented and used for the injured spine, mainly by orthopaedic surgeons for orthopaedic operations. In the early 'modern era' of the care of people with a TSCI, some surgeons, usually orthopaedic surgeons, used a variety of metal plates, however with no obvious benefit to the patient, and indeed many complications ensued. I remember reading a scientific paper in an international conference on spinal injuries in the USA, in the 1950s. I mentioned my concern, and gave examples of poor plating for some TSCI patients, and included mention of the use of the Harrington instrumentation of rods and distraction hooks. The Chairman asked if Dr Harrington would care to comment: I had no idea, till then, that that distinguished orthopaedic surgeon was in the audience! But he turned out to be a very nice gentleman. He thanked me, and went on to say that he agreed with me, that the instrumentation with his name was unsuitable for the treatment of TSCI patients. Their use was for operations on some patients with severe spinal deformities, such as scoliosis. Indeed, yes; and I had shown slides to make my point – the Harrington system would require to securely fix the spine by including two vertebrae above and two below 'the damaged vertebra'; bad for the nurses and the physiotherapists and also for the patient.

There are certain principles that must be carefully considered regarding the occasional surgical (operative) treatment for the spine in patients with a TSCI including open wounds.

Important special procedures for certain TSCI patients

- Functional electrical stimulations (FES). These are specialised computer-electrically controlled systems used to stimulate paralysed limbs, especially the hands and the legs. Some results show real promise.
- An operation to electrically stimulate the sacral nerves supplying the paralysed urinary bladder. I worked with a Consultant urological surgeon, usually Mr Jack Newsam. A lumbo-sacral laminectomy was carried out, and an intradural approach, to expose the sacral 2, 3 and 4 nerve roots in the cauda equina. With necessary magnification, as the nerves are very small, each root was separated into anterior and posterior parts. Then each anterior root was electrically stimulated to study the effects on the patient's bladder, rectum and pelvic floor muscles, carefully monitoring each aspect of the procedure. It usually appeared that S4 was the main nerve for bladder emptying. The nerves were specially 'housed', and leads from the roots were passed up from the spinal operation site, and were brought subcutaneously under the abdominal skin to a radio receiver. Subsequently, the patient could stimulate the sacral nerves by placing a small triradiate transmitter over the abdominal receiver, with resultant emptying of the bladder. It was an ingenious, very helpful procedure.
- Phrenic nerve stimulation. With a complete SC lesion at or above the third cervical (C3) spinal cord segment there will be paralysis of the diaphragm (the largest muscle in the body), a most serious situation indeed, usually requiring a tracheostomy and a respirator. Expert medical respiratory and physiotherapy and nursing treatment are vital. As shown by Glen and his associates in the USA (1980), electrical stimulation of the paralysed diaphragm can result in satisfactory diaphragmatic pacing, and the respirator will not be required. In some ways the procedure is similar to that described above for sacral nerve root stimulation, except that the nerves to be stimulated are the two phrenic nerves, which can be easily exposed in the neck (or in the abdomen for children).

Research studies

There are many important research studies on the intrinsic neuro-pathological, vascular, chemical changes that occur in the injured spinal cord. Attempts have been made to control them, and indeed to reverse them, but so far without success. The use of large doses of dexamethasone (a gluco–corticoid) administered very soon after a TSCI was heralded as a real advance in the control of the above cord changes, with some clinical improvement. But my understanding, unfortunately, is that there was no real, practical neurological benefit.

As I write this, there is growing interest in, and indeed hope for, the use of human embryonic stem cells, to be introduced directly to the site of the spinal cord damage, to control and reverse the TSCI.

If there is still no evidence of neurological function distal to the site of the injured spinal cord for twenty-four or more hours, the lesion is complete and permanent.

Examples of a TSCI

A stab wound of the spine

This is an example of a patient with an acute, severe TSCI requiring urgent surgical treatment. A fifteen-year-old youth was involved in a fracas in a central public garden in Edinburgh, when one of the boys struck him in the middle of his back with a knife. The youth was felled, with severe paralysis of his legs. He was transferred forthwith to our department, coming under my care. Examination showed a very anxious youth. The weapon had been removed from his back, and there was no leakage of cerebrospinal fluid from the small, vertical stab wound. He had a partial hemi-spinal cord neurological deficit (known as the 'Brown-Sequard Syndrome'). Plain radiographs of the spine were normal, but an imaging study revealed an intradural mass at the mid-thoracic (T7–T8) level of the spine, compressing the spinal cord. Urgent surgery was carried out. I found that the lesion was an acute subdural haematoma (clot of blood), severely compressing the spinal cord. The clot was removed. (We had ascertained on the admission of the patient that he was not on any anticoagulant drug, nor did he have a blood coagulation disorder.)

He made a full neurological recovery (Harris 2004).

21. Dr Wilder Penfield

22. Miss Estelle Adamson, Matron, Western General Hospital, Edinburgh.
Courtesy of The Scotsman Publications Ltd, Edinburgh

23. Sir Hugh Cairns. Courtesy of British Medical Association, Publishing Group, London.
J. Neurol. Neurosurg. Psychiat. 1985, 48: 965–976

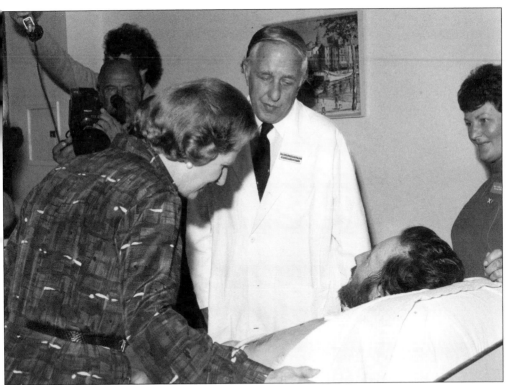

24. *The Prime Minister: Mrs (later, Lady) Thatcher visiting my ward in the Department of Surgical Neurology (DSN), Edinburgh*

25. *Three Consultant surgeons retiring on the same day, in September 1987 from the Royal Infirmary of Edinburgh and Edinburgh University. Left: Mr Philip Myerscough, Obstetrics and Gynaecology; Centre: myself; Right: Mr Tom McNair, General Surgeon.* Courtesy of The Scotsman Publications Ltd, Edinburgh

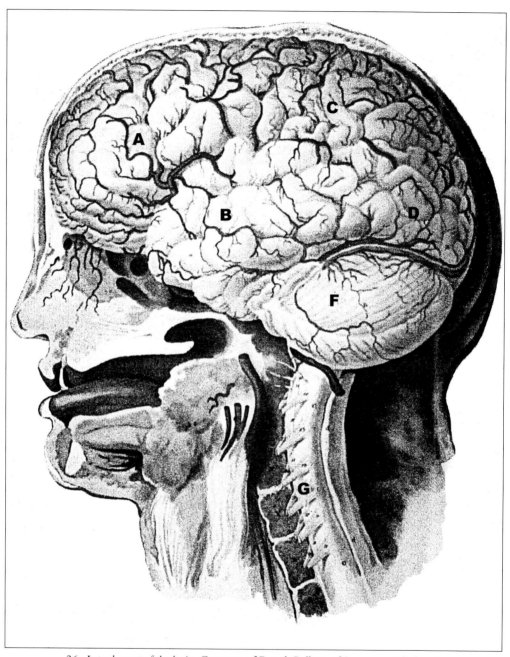

26. Lateral aspect of the brain. Courtesy of Royal College of Surgeons, Edinburgh

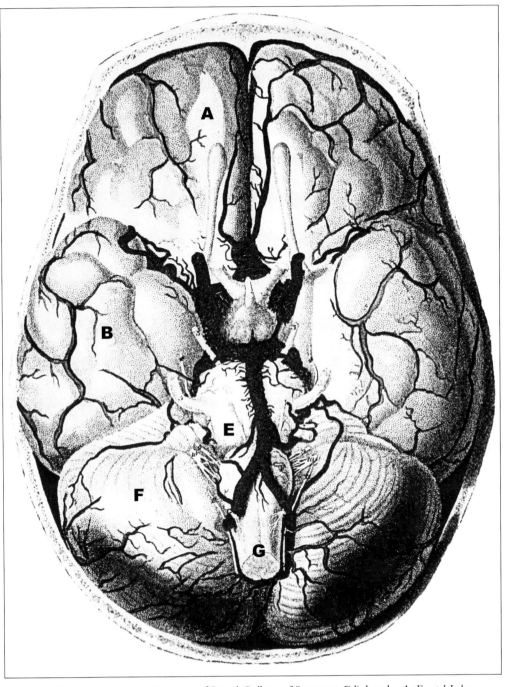

27. *The base of the brain.* Courtesy of Royal College of Surgeons, Edinburgh. *A: Frontal Lobe;*
B: Temporal Lobe; C: Parietal Lobe; D: Occipital Lobe; E: Brain Stem; F: Cerebellum; G: Uppermost part of Cervical
Spinal Cord. Also shown is the base of the brain, the anterior, middle, posterior, basilar and vertebral arteries

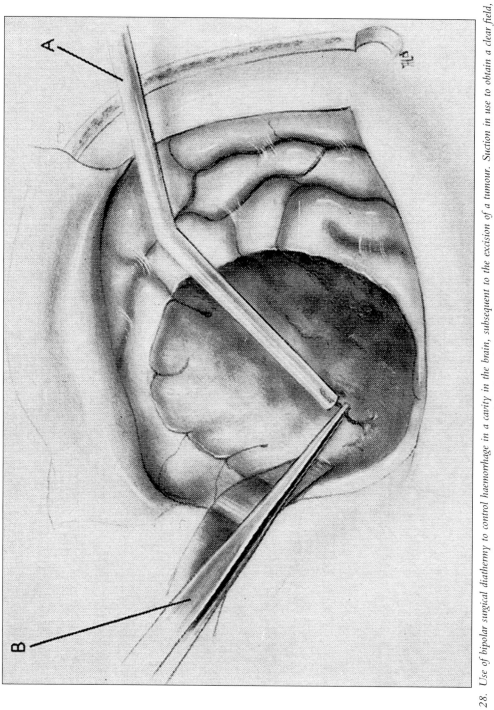

28. *Use of bipolar surgical diathermy to control haemorrhage in a cavity in the brain, subsequent to the excision of a tumour. Suction in use to obtain a clear field, to show the small bleeding artery*

29. Dr Hans Berger at the age of 52 years. Discoverer of the cerebral (brain) waves (EEG)

30. The first ever EEG machine in the world. (Dr Hans Berger) 1924

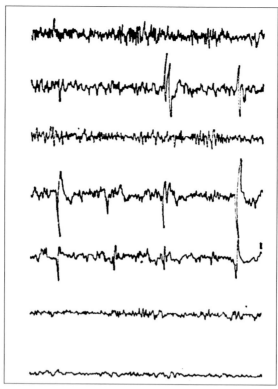

31. *Part of an electroencephalogram (EEG) revealing spike waves in the recording, typical of epilepsy*

32. *Opening ceremony of the Hans Berger Symposium on Epilepsy, University of Edinburgh, July 1973.*
In the front row, left to right, Professor Ramamurthi, Professor Gillingham, Mrs Dott, Professor Dott, Professor Sano

Traumatic cervical 5–6 subluxation (Subluxation: a partial dislocation)

An adult male sustained a severe neck injury in a car accident, resulting in incomplete tetraparesis. Skull traction with Gardner-Wells tongs was applied, with the patient lying supine on a Stryker turning frame and the tongs resting on the special support of the frame. In the usual way the weights were steadily increased to a safe limit but unfortunately, the subluxation could not be reduced. Therefore, knowing the risks of not reducing the subluxation, an operation (the type I had described and published in 1966) was performed. A general anaesthetic was given and then the patient was turned over on the frame to a prone position. Open reduction of the subluxation was now carried out. The spinous processes of C5 and C6 were wired together with stainless steel wire, and were then covered with methyl methylmethacrylate, to securely fix the spine. The wound was closed and the patient turned over to lie supine. Then an anterior interbody bony fusion of the bodies of C5 and C6 was carried out. The patient was allowed to sit up two days post-operatively, and was steadily mobilised. A good result was obtained.

Lumbar spine fractures

Acute trauma to the lumbar spine can cause displacement of vertebrae, with tearing of the dura and the arachnoid (the coverings of the lumbar and sacral nerve roots, the cauda equina), so that they prolapse into the spinal canal where they will adhere and result in serious, probably progressive lumbar and sacral nerve damage with clinical consequences – that is, if the condition is not promptly diagnosed and dealt with by a neurosurgeon, exposing the damaged area, replacing the nerves and closing the dura. I described the condition in 1963.

The consequences of not diagnosing, or if there has been a long delay in diagnosing and treating the condition discussed above (lumbar spine fractures, with dural and arachnoid membrane tears, and prolapse of lumbar and sacral nerve roots), will be serious, with long term increasing neurological deficits, and marked adhesions and matting together of the prolapsed nerve roots. Furthermore, if an operation is at that stage carried out, it will be discovered that these nerve roots cannot safely be separated and replaced inside the spinal dural–arachnoid membranes.

Spinal units

Over the years I have been invited to visit and give lectures and to discuss the institution, building, equipping and staffing of spinal units in a number of countries and cities, including New Delhi, India; Cornell University, New York; North-Western University, Chicago; Saudi Arabia; Greece; Cyprus; Cairo.

Sport for disabled people

The history of sport for disabled people, initially for upper or lower limb amputees, goes back to the times of the Napoleonic Wars. In World War I, in the UK, volleyball and swimming events took place (Silver, 2003).

In relation to World War II wheelchair sports for spinal paralysed ex-service personnel in Britain was introduced in Stoke Mandeville Hospital in England under the direction of the inspiring Dr (later, Sir) Ludwig Guttmann. There were increasing numbers of participants. As time went on many different types of sports were introduced, and competitions were organised, nationally and internationally, including the now famous Paralympic Games.

With a nucleus of people, in 1963 I formed the Scottish Sports Association for the Disabled (SSAD), later called Scottish Disability Sport (SDS). We attracted several devoted, dedicated and knowledgeable people, and the organisation developed, covering the whole of Scotland, and encompassing a wide variety of sports for disabled people with many different disabilities, including paralysis, amputees, visual disorders, deafness, and learning difficulties. Several sports included wheelchair involvements. The sports include basketball, swimming, angling, shinty, golf, badminton, snooker, curling, bowls, archery, athletics, boating, skiing, and football. There are very real physical and mental health benefits from sport, with improved self esteem, confidence, facing challenges, having new opportunities to travel and to be involved in communal affairs, and indeed to help to obtain suitable employment – and become a taxpayer. The general public has become more aware of the disabilities that many people have, and there is good attendance at the sporting events. Facilities for the sports have greatly improved. In 1970 we had the British Commonwealth Paraplegic Games in Edinburgh. Some of the city buses were modified so that wheelchair competitors could be transported. A request had been made to advise on having complete access for all disabled people in the new Meadowbank Sports Stadium and the new Common-wealth Swimming Pool in Edinburgh. I accepted this important request.

Disabled sportswomen and sportsmen can excel in their sport; examples include a wheelchair bound lady who was paraplegic, Mrs Margaret Harmain, a South African, an excellent archer who competed against able bodied international archers, coming 8th out of 48 competitors. Several years ago a team of wheelchair bound basketball players beat a major New York, USA able-bodied team – they also required to play in wheelchairs! Certainly there is no lack of skill and determination in disabled sports people.

After some years I demitted office of Chairmanship of SSAD and I was appointed the Honorary President. The retiring Chairman, Richard Brickley, with his team of dedicated officials and supporters has been doing a wonderful job for disabled Scottish sports people. The movement has snowballed, and is very popular with people with physical disabilities and also with those who have learning problems. I would stress that sport for disabled people, both adults and children, is, of course, not only competitive at local, national or international levels, but is also, if I may use the term, recreational – and of course enjoyable – but with obvious physical health and psychological aspects, not always obvious.

The paralympic games in Tokyo

The paraplegic athletes and the officials had all been staying in the Olympic Village in Tokyo. The British, Dutch, Israeli and Irish teams and officials were returning in a KLM plane. About halfway to Anchorage, Alaska, the Captain came over to me as I was 'the doctor in charge' and was quite young then, to say that one of the four engines was not a hundred per cent and required ground staff attention. He asked me, knowing that the great majority of people in the full plane were spinal paralysed, although they were excellent athletes, if he should fly on to Anchorage, where there would be, unfortunately, poor facilities for the athletes, or return to Tokyo. What a question! However I was in no doubt that we should return to Tokyo. An announcement was made, the plane turned round and we went back to Japan. However, typical of the Japanese, the Olympic Village was no more, it had already been demolished! It would take over an hour and a half for everyone to leave the plane, then to go 'somewhere', presumably to some hotels. The engine was busily being repaired. We just made it in time! So we all settled down, refuelling was in Anchorage, then off to London, Heathrow, where everyone now returned to their own country. I did not count the number of hours that all of the paralysed sports women and men had remained in the plane. They certainly did very well. Several had the medals that they had won in Tokyo.

Autonomic dysreflexia

A condition called autonomic dysreflexia may occur in some people who have a high spinal cord lesion from injury or disease. The condition may arise if one or more of such factors as a full urinary bladder, prolonged perineal skin pressure, significant pressure ulcers, limb muscle spasms, cystitis, or bladder calculi exist. The main symptoms include headache, chest tightness, flushing and sweating. The blood pressure rises, and occasionally there are serious brain disturbances and even a stroke. I knew that some elite high spinal level paraplegic athletes had discovered that their performances in certain sports for the disabled could be boosted by inducing autonomic dysreflexia; for example by drinking a lot of fluids and filling their bladder maximally. But there were obvious real risks and dangers, and it was strongly recommended that such 'boosting' should be disallowed. (Harris 1994).

Surgical treatment of pain

Pain is a cardinal medical symptom.

If pain is due to a disorder such as a protruded intervertebral disc or acute appendicitis, it can obviously be managed, indeed cured, by operative removal of the offending disc or appendix, and in most medical situations dealing with the cause of the pain in this way is effective. Non-addictive analgesic drugs can control many 'ordinary pains', such as a headache or a pulled muscle. But there are also certain painful conditions where the response to non-addictive analgesics is very poor or totally ineffective. This is where the neurosurgeon may be able to help, to deal with what is known as intractable pain. Some such situations are now quite briefly discussed. We had been dealing with them in our department.

The whole physiology, anatomy, pathology, and also neurological, psychological and psychiatric aspects of pain is a huge, very important subject.

Intractable pain includes such situations and conditions as paroxysmal trigeminal neuralgia, malignant disease, phantom limb pain, amputation stump pain, and post-herpetic neuralgia.

Pain clinics are available in many hospitals, and in Edinburgh we have an excellent one in our department. It is headed by a consultant anaesthetist, and includes a physician, a surgeon, a psychiatrist, a psychologist and ancillary personnel.

Pain arising from organic lesions is transmitted up – mainly, in the spino-thalamic tracts, which are in the anterolateral aspect of the spinal cord. The fibres cross over, so that, for example, pain sensation in the left leg will be transmitted up the right anterolateral aspect of the spinal cord to the brain, where the pain is perceived.

(1) Martin in 1911 (Spiller and Martin) carried out the first *anterolateral cordotomy* for intractable pain. The result of the procedure can be good, but the level of thermo-analgesia will drop several segments, and the effects tend to wear off; this is not a good procedure for the treatment of 'benign' causes of pain, such as nerve root pain from an intervertebral lumbar disc disorder (such as 'a scarred root'). The operation involves a cut of 3, 4 or 5 mm in the anterolateral aspect of the spinal cord; then the general anaesthetic is reversed so that the patient's co-operation can be obtained, by a doctor testing and checking the upper level of loss of pain sensation; if necessary the incision can carefully be deepened and the sensory level is rechecked. Then the general anaesthetic is once more given, for surgical wound closure.

(2) *Dorsal column stimulation.* This is a procedure for certain forms of intractable pain, but has not gained much favour in our department. It involves a spinal operation to implant a radio-telemetric apparatus in the patient over the dorsal columns of the spinal cord. The wound is closed. An external transmitter is then used to stimulate the dorsal columns.

(3) *Intraspinal, subarachnoid injection of 5% phenol in pantopaque.* Dr A. S. Brown, Consultant anaesthetist in our department, treated a large series of patients with that type of treatment, 80 per cent of whom had malignant disease, who were completely relieved.

(4) *Paroxysmal trigeminal neuralgia.* This is common. There is extremely severe pain – like a 'red hot feeling' – occurring in adults, but occasionally in young people who have multiple sclerosis. It affects one side of the face, usually in the cheek-nose region, or in the lower jaw region, less often in the forehead. Trigger areas – touching the area, speaking, chewing. There are no neurological signs. It usually responds well to an anticonvulsant drug such as carbamazepine (tegretol), but not always, and the effect may fade. There are a number of neurosurgical procedures, including injection of absolute alcohol in tiny doses through the cheek, into the trigeminal ganglion in the head (using X-ray control); or by making a radiofrequency lesion. Another procedure is to approach the trigeminal nerve by an intracranial operation, and then, with the aid of a dissecting microscope, to

decompress the sensory part of the trigeminal nerve. We are familiar with all of these procedures. Important complications may ensue if the patient's eye (the cornea) becomes desensitised as a result of the surgical therapy and then a corneal ulcer can develop, which is serious; the ala of the nose may also ulcerate resulting in an unpleasant cosmetic disfigurement. Both these complications can be speedily and fully dealt with by carrying out cervical sympathectomy (better, and long lasting, a superior cervical ganglion-ectomy (Harris 1951)).

(5) *Paroxysmal glossopharyngeal neuralgia.* This is much less common than paroxysmal trigeminal neuralgia, but the pain and its 'behaviour' are much the same, this time affecting the tongue and back of the throat. If not responding to carbamazepine, the treatment is to expose the glosso-pharyngeal nerve intracranially and simply divide it. There will be no complications.

(6) *Post-herpetic neuralgia.* This may occur in older people, after an attack of herpes zoster; the virus causing this can affect any sensory nerve in the body. This has some relationship to chickenpox. The pain is absolutely awful, burning, chronic, and relentless, making the poor patient quite miserable, and he may become depressed. If there is a shooting element in the pain, carbamazapine might help. Non-addictive analgesics are of no real avail. Unfortunately, no surgical treatment is beneficial.

(7) *Hormonal ablation.* A number of procedures have been and some may continue to be used to treat intractable pain from advanced cancer of the breast or of the prostate. (See section on pituitary gland ablation.)

Giraffe

An amusing after-thought for a neurosurgeon: a nightmare, requiring to operate on a giraffe with a cervical disc protrusion! Like humans, a giraffe has seven cervical vertebrae, but each is huge, as are the inververtebral discs.

CHAPTER 4

Some overseas medical involvements

The British Council

AN INVITATION WAS RECEIVED FROM the British Council in London for me, accompanied by my wife, Sheelagh, to go on a British Council Medical Specialist Tour of India, from 8 September to 11 October 1986. The objectives were to visit several medical centres in India, in particular neuroscience centres, in Universities and in hospitals, to meet medical and administrative personnel, noting and reporting on the facilities, clinical and research activities, and monitoring medical undergraduate and postgraduate medical, nursing, rehabilitation and associated staff personnel, and the examination arrangements. I was also to give lectures, participate in seminars, and 'meet the media' – television, radio and the press. The whole tour was immaculately planned, and the British Council staff and local people were most friendly and helpful. Cities included Bangalore, Madras, Vellore and New Delhi. My lectures included these topics: spinal injuries; spinal paralysis; cervical disc protrusions; cervical spondylosis; head injuries; and brain tumours.

A common cause of spinal disease, and medical spinal paralysis in India was tuberculosis (Pott's paraplegia). For the first time, I was required to give a public oration; my topic was 'Broken necks and broken backs. Then and now'. On another occasion, I was invited to give the 'Lakshimipathi Oration'. The title of this lecture was 'The Use of Lasers in Medical and Surgical Practice'. Dr Lakshimipathi was a famous Indian doctor, an ophthalmologist, a skilled physician, and a great humanitarian. He founded the wonderful Madras Medical College in 1957, being the first neurosurgical department in India. I was honoured to receive the Dr A. L. Lakshimipathi medal and prize, the latter being a silver Davi. The doctor was the father-in-law of the doyen of Indian neuro-surgeons, my very good friend, Professor B. Ramamurthi (usually known as 'Ram').

In New Delhi, Sheelagh and I met General Chahal, a senior neuro-surgeon and rehabilitation specialist, Mr H. C. Sarin, a senior Indian civil servant and President of the Indian Mountaineering Foundation, and Major

H. P. S. Ahluwalia – the famous Mount Everest climber, who, most unfortunately, some time later, was shot in a fracas and became permanently paraplegic. I was an adviser and consultant, discussing the plans and organisation of the new, unique, custom built spinal unit in New Delhi, the first in India. The Patron in Chief of the project was Mr Rajiv Gandhi, Prime Minister of India.

Burma

The Burmese Government asked us in the Department of Neurosurgery in Edinburgh if we would possibly assist with the introduction and the development of neurosurgery in Rangoon, Burma. We were delighted to do so. Then sometime later, the Burmese Government invited Sheelagh and me to visit Burma to study the progress being made, and to give any further advice. Our guide and escort was a fine young man, Dr Myo Myint, whom we had trained in Edinburgh. I was impressed that neurosurgery was going on well, though slowly.

One day we were shown an unusual hip prosthesis. It was beautifully carved out of ivory. Similar ones had been surgically implanted in patients, apparently with a successful outcome.

We had an extensive tour of Burma, including visits to Mandalay (where a second neurosurgical unit was being planned), and Pagan, indeed going right up to the Chinese border. Sheelagh reminded me that Aaron, her brother, had been lost for a long time in Burma during World War II. He was an Army captain of a tank and was eventually found.

During our stay we met Government ministers, doctors and nurses. Everyone was very friendly.

Boston

In Boston, Mass., USA I gave several lectures, including one on 'Pituitary Ablation by Y^{90} (Yttrium) Implantations for Advancing Diabetic Retinopathy: a Further Report after 5 Years' Experience'; and a paper on 'Aetiological Factors Involved in Intracranial Hypertension'. Harvard medical teaching was based on education, research and patient care. The Countway Library was most impressive, architecturally and with over 400,000 books and some 6,000 periodicals. It cost 6¼ million dollars to build. I spent an interesting time with Mr Harold Blomquest, the Senior Librarian.

Japan, Israel and Egypt

I clearly remember attending an International Meeting of Neurosurgeons in Japan. Word came through that Egypt and Israel were going to be at war, and neurosurgeons from these countries were forthwith to return home. We had all been good friends for several years; we shook hands and bade farewell, hoping that all in fact would turn out satisfactorily.

Peru

In Peru, in July 1977, I visited several medical doctors, including the neurosurgeon Dr Fernando Cabiesis in Cusco, and gave several lectures. Sheelagh accompanied me. Dr Cabiesis had a deep interest in the Inca civilisation, and indeed was the curator of the Inca museum. I received a copy of his beautiful book, *Gods and Disease. Medicine in Ancient Peru* (1974). We learnt about the early culture of these people and their unique way of life. They had no written language, but built fine buildings and made striking sculptures – some showing people with bulging cheeks from chewing coca (cocaine) leaves. I understand that Sigmund Freud got his awful habit of using cocaine from Peru.

Some Incas carried out the remarkable procedure of head binding of babies' heads, using boards and binding material, to influence the permanent shape of the person's head. The aim apparently was to produce heads of a particular shape, for example, abnormally broad, or long, or tall. In babies and young children the bones of the skull have fibrous tissue joints, and do not join securely by sutures for some time. The reason for head binding was apparently to identify different tribes or sects.

In the Inca museum, Dr Cabiesis showed us the skull of the tyrant, the Spaniard Pissaro, who with his soldiers plundered and slaughtered Incas, seeking Inca gold. Some of the Incas had gone up to Machu Picchu. Sheelagh and I were very interested in many aspects of the remarkable Inca civilisation. We spent some time in Cusco. As a wonderful memento, Dr Cabiesis gave me an Inca knife. We remembered being in the wonderful train which had to negotiate the railway which included some hair-pin bends.

CHAPTER 5

Medical and other organisations

The Royal College of Surgeons of Edinburgh (RCSE)

THE ROYAL COLLEGE OF SURGEONS of Edinburgh is one of the oldest medical colleges in the world, being founded in 1505 and receiving a Royal Charter, from King James IV of Scotland, in 1506.

It serves several purposes: as a post-graduate teaching centre; an examining body, setting up and maintaining professional standards; holding surgical symposia and conferences; and providing information on current and developing aspects of the surgical sciences. It has become a large surgical international organisation of high repute, giving a notable service to humanity. It has a very fine library.

The Fellowship diploma is highly prized and is recognised as such, worldwide. There are now over 16,000 Fellows and Members, 6,000 of them residing in the UK.

I have served on committees of the College, including the Library Committee, and represented the College in the development of the University of Edinburgh Erskine Library.

In 2005 my wife and I attended the wonderful Quincentenary celebrations which attracted a large number of Fellows and their spouses from all over the world. This was truly a grand event.

Famous past Fellows of the College include Lord Lister, Joseph Bell, James Syme and Robert Knox. Bell was apparently the inspiration that Sir Arthur Conan Doyle used for his fictional but famous detective, Sherlock Holmes.

Just one amusing, personal story of the College. When sitting the Fellowship exam (in 1948), in the Surgical Pathology part I, I was shown one of the bottled pathology specimens. The questioning went: the examiner: 'What is this pathological specimen?' Answer: 'A testicle showing a tumour, Sir.' 'What type?' 'Probably a seminoma, Sir.' (Then there was a discussion on tumours of the testicle.) 'Anything unusual about that testicle?' 'It's very large.' 'Why?' (I knew the answer, because, like many medical students sitting the Fellowship exam, I had spent some time studying in the museum.) 'Could be a horse's testicle, Sir.' And it was, and I passed.

88

For many surgeons, in the UK and elsewhere, the College is a happy fascinating place, bringing back fond memories of fellowship.

The College motto is *Hinc Sanitas* (From here to health).

The Royal College of Physicians of Edinburgh (RCPE)

I am pleased to be a Fellow of this famous College, with a history extending back to the seventeenth century, formed by a nucleus of Edinburgh physicians, to organise and improve the standards of Edinburgh medicine. The College obtained its Royal Charter from Charles II in 1681.

It has steadily grown in size and in numbers of Fellows and Members and is a worldwide body for the advancement of medicine. Worldwide there are more than 7,000 Fellows and Members, practising in some fifty specialties in over eighty countries.

The College has an excellent medical library.

Like the other Royal Colleges, Medical and Surgical in Scotland, the RCPE is a very important examining body for post-graduate medical students, and is a major educational organisation.

The Royal College of Physicians and Surgeons of Glasgow (RCP and S Glas)

This was founded in 1599, with the grant of a charter from King James VI to Mr Peter Lowe, surgeon.

The College has some 8,500 Fellows and Members, physicians, surgeons and dentists, scattered throughout the world, and has the aim of advancing good medical practice. It is an excellent, very friendly body. Thanks to Mr Sloan Robertson, Head of the Department of Neurosurgery in the Glasgow region, I was delighted to be made a Fellow, *ad eundem*.

Included in a roll of distinguished Fellows are Joseph Black, William Cullen and John Moore.

The Society of British Neurological Surgeons (SBNS)

This Society which serves the whole of the UK was founded eighty-two years ago, in 1926. It is the second oldest neurosurgical society in the world (the Society of Neurosurgical Surgeons in the USA is four years older).

The key founding father of the SBNS was Geoffrey Jefferson (of Manchester), and he and Norman Dott, Charles Balance, Percy Sargent, Wilfrid Trotter, Bathe Rowling, Donald Armour and James Learmonth established the Society at a meeting and dinner in the Athenaeum Club in London. The constitution and by-laws date from 1938. Initially there were fifteen Full members; currently there are 219 Full members, and just over a hundred Associate members.

It was decided to hold two scientific meetings a year; and also to have some overseas meetings. The SBNS helped to form a number of neurosurgical daughter societies in Europe. I well remember attending and participating in early meetings, including some in Europe; these meetings included sessions observing neurosurgical operations being carried out by neurosurgeons of the hosts for the meeting; but this was later discontinued, because as time went on too many doctors were attending the meetings. Nowadays of course, there are wonderful audio-visual facilities for the audience.

The SBNS is a major scientific body, with increasing activities and involvements in the training and in the service aspects of the specialty of neurological surgery. Sometimes the term 'neurosurgery' is used; and indeed, both Trotter and Dott preferred the term 'surgical neurology'; the use of that designation should, one presumes, be obvious.

In September 1984, I organised the combined meeting of the Society of British Neurological Surgeons (SBNS) and the Association of British Neurologists (ABN) in Edinburgh. But on the evening of the banquet I received an urgent message informing me that my dear mother was severely ill and was being taken by ambulance to the Royal Infirmary. I rushed there. Expert cardiological care was being given, but my brother, David and I witnessed the failure of all possible resuscitative measures, and our beloved mother died.

The World Federation of Neurosurgical Societies (WFNS)

I was elected to Council, and I represented the Society of British Neurological Surgeons (SBNS) on the WFNS for twelve years, and also the Neurotraumatology Committee of the WFNS – the NTC.

The WFNS was founded in 1955, with Sir Geoffrey Jefferson as the first President.

The aims of the WFNS are to facilitate the personal association of neurosurgeons world wide, encouraging the advancement of neurosurgery in all of its many aspects and discussing and resolving neurosurgical problems internationally.

The first Congress of the Federation was held in 1957 in Brussels, in the presence of His Majesty the King of the Belgians. It was a huge meeting as it included members of several neural sciences: medical and surgical neurology, electroencephalography, neuropathology, neuroradiology, and the International League against Epilepsy! Sheelagh and I remember it well, including the banquet, which was held in the very large, lovely Palais de Justice on a beautiful summer evening, with an orchestra playing 'Around the World in 80 Days'.

Subsequently the WFNS met in different countries, without the other specialty organisations, and included an International Congress of Neuro-surgeons. One committee of the Federation was formed in 1965, the Neurotraumatology Committee (NTC), with the aim to meet regularly in different countries with the remit to study, research, teach, and provide literature on the various aspects of injuries to the nervous system. I was elected to it in 1973, becoming vice-chairman. In 1982, the meeting was held in Edinburgh. The title was rather long: International Conference on Recent Advances in Neurotraumatology: ICRAN. This was accepted and continues to be in use everywhere for our meetings. We had a fine, well attended conference, attracting doctors from many countries. I am reminded that prices for the conference in 1982 were really low compared to nowadays: Registration was £90 (included lunch, morning coffee, and afternoon tea). The banquet (not just 'a dinner'!) was £17.50. A City of Edinburgh tour was £10 and a Bowhill tour, to the Duke of Buccleuch's home, including high tea, £15. Bed and breakfast in Edinburgh University Halls of Residence was £9.50 and a deluxe hotel per person only £27.

The Proceedings of the conference were published.

Other ICRAN meetings have been held in some different cities and countries, including Washington, USA; Copenhagen; New York; Tokyo; San Paulo, Brazil; Munich; New Delhi; Seville; and in 1997 ICRAN was held in Moscow, with an invitation from the Russian Government, through the Russian Association of Neurosurgeons, organised by Professor Konovalov and Professor Potapov, who was the secretary of the NTC. The meeting was held on board a ship, the top deck of which was a lecture theatre, and it sailed down the Volga River, then returned to Moscow. All participated in lecturing and in discussions, and indeed also in sampling various excellent vodkas! My telephone calls and faxes to Professor Potapov, our Secretary, revealed the source of '007': the telephone code for Moscow (and for James Bond!). Sheelagh and I then went on to St Petersburg, and in the airport there a pleasant, well dressed gentleman offered to help us to deal with our luggage and to obtain a taxi. We also ran across him later, coming down in the lift of our hotel, and, indeed, also when we attended the theatre to watch the Bolshoi Ballet – he was sitting two rows in front of us. Coincidence!

The Royal Society of Edinburgh (RSE)

The Royal Society of Edinburgh is 'Scotland's National Academy'. It received its Royal Charter in 1783, and is unique in Great Britain as its Fellowship represents excellence across the whole field of the academic disciplines, including professional, technical and business. The aim is to advance learning and useful knowledge. It has wide ranging involvements, with lectures, symposia, exhibitions, debates, and the provision of independent advice to Parliament, the Government, and other important bodies, and has wide links with appropriate bodies internationally. There are 1,300 Fellows. I was elected in 1967.

Renowned past Presidents include Sir Walter Scott and Lord Kelvin; and legendary Honorary Fellows include Benjamin Franklin, Goethe, and Einstein.

The Scottish Association of Neurological Sciences (SANS)

During the seventies, I felt that it could be a good idea to invite doctors from all of the Scottish 'neural specialists': medical and surgical neurology, neuropathology, neurophysiology, neuro-radiology, basic neural science doctors, and so on, to foregather and meet once a year in rotation in one of the Scottish Universities, Edinburgh, Glasgow, St Andrews, Dundee and Aberdeen. Each specialty of course has its own named organisation, but the SANS would bring all the various neural specialists together for 'cross fertilisation', to hear papers read and discussed. I discussed my idea with Mr Alastair Paterson, a Glasgow neurosurgeon, who agreed with me, and we went ahead. I am pleased to say that the SANS continues to flourish.

The International Medical Society of Paraplegia (IMSOP)/The International Spinal Cord Society (ISCOS)

With the steadily increasing worldwide interest in the many aspects of traumatic and non-traumatic spinal cord and spinal nerve root injuries, and of spinal congenital abnormalities it was clearly necessary to form an international organisation for the study and treatment of patients with such lesions, and this was undertaken in 1961 by Dr (later, Sir) Ludwig Guttmann and a group of equally interested and involved doctors. I was a founder member, a council member, a Fellow, and later, a medalist, of what was initially called the International Medical Society of Paraplegia (IMSOP).

The name was later changed to the International Spinal Cord Society (ISCOS). This was and is the only worldwide body dedicated to the study and improvement of the lives of people with a spinal cord lesion.

The journal of IMSOP/ISCOS was born in 1963, with Ludwig Guttmann as the first Editor. I was elected Assistant Editor. The initial name of the journal was *Paraplegia*. The aim was to unite the Society's widely scattered members, and also to be available worldwide to medical and paramedical people, acting as a core facility of scientific information and reporting on the considerable advances being made in the whole complex of the important field of spinal cord injury, traumatic and non-traumatic. There had not previously been a suitable journal to serve its several purposes: the publication of original scientific papers; case reports; and correspondence. The initial publishers were E. and S. Livingstone, Edinburgh and London; and subsequently and currently, the Nature Publishing Group, London.

I served for seventeen years as Assistant Editor, and was then elected Editor. This was my opportunity, over a short period of time, to make some changes in the journal. These included changing the name to the more appropriate one of *Spinal Cord*; increasing the number of issues per year to six, then to twelve, becoming a monthly journal; making some changes in the Editorial Board, taking into account the different special aspects of spinal cord injury and also the geographical spread of the Society members; to have some Regional organised issues (for example, the USA and Japan); changing the typescript, and also the page size to A4; to use the Vancouver reference system; to introduce a 'case of the month' series; to have very (and I mean this) minimal anecdotal contributions; to discontinue having abstracts of papers in French and in German, but to have everything in English; to accept the American spelling of words in contributions from North America; to ensure that every paper submitted for possible publication was peer reviewed by two or sometimes more appropriate senior doctors. I also decided to change the colour of the journal, from dusty green to a nice bright orange colour. At the council meeting when this was mentioned, one member said loudly, in a strong, Irish accent, 'Oh, no, not orange!' but orange it became!

I greatly enjoyed my term as Editor of *Spinal Cord*, but after seventeen years I decided to demit this office, having already served the Society as Assistant Editor for seventeen years: a total of thirty-four years! I have the honour to continue as Emeritus Editor.

I agreed with Dr Stephen Lock (past Editor of the British Medical Journal) that 'all editing is a balancing act. The editor must serve not only his science, but also his readers in their moments of relaxation and thoughtfulness'.

There were many pleasantries, but also a few problems with the journal, such as fraud, and to ensure that items had not been previously published 'somewhere, sometime'; concern about items on 'miracle breakthrough'; and to discourage multiple and salami reports.

Certainly an editor requires moral courage and a sense of fair play.

The Thistle Foundation

To commemorate the death of his officer son in World War II, Sir Francis Tudsbury had a large custom-made complex built in Edinburgh for the housing accommodation of disabled war veterans and their families. There were special houses, excellent rehabilitation facilities including physio-therapy and occupational therapy, hydrotherapy, and sport facilities. For many years I was a member of the Board of Management.

The Rotary Club of Edinburgh

The Club was founded in 1912. Rotary is a unique international organisation; the motto is: 'Service Above Self'. There are a wide range of activities and involvements, with a philosophy of friendship and service, with international connections and an understanding and interchange of students on an Ambassadorial Scholar Scheme. The genius of Rotary has been to respond to the needs of the day, from child welfare to abolishing poliomyelitis by carrying out international immunisation programmes. Other special involvements include the institution of wells for the supply of clean, safe water in developing countries; and another is arranging facilities for peoples to learn and speak English.

Our members are drawn from business, the professions, academia, the civil service, clergy, and the police.

In my year as President 1991–92 activities included a charity film premiere of *The Medicine Man*, starring Sean Connery. We were able to donate over £10,000 towards the Development Fund for an extension of the Royal Hospital for Sick Children in Edinburgh, and were delighted to have the lovely Duchess of Kent as our Patron and guest of honour, and presented her with the highest Rotary International honour: making her a Paul Harris Fellow (he was the Founder of the Rotary movement, in Chicago, USA, in 1905). Our Club over the years has founded new Clubs in the UK. In my year of office we also helped to found the first Rotary Club in the Ukraine, the Rotary Club of Kiev. I have the distinction of being elected a Paul Harris Fellow.

The media

In March 1958 we in our Department were invited by the BBC to undertake the first of a new series of programmes, with the title *Your Life in their Hands*. We accepted, although it would be transmitted to the world live in black and white TV. At that time there was, apparently, no prior video recording and editing.

This proved to be an interesting and challenging task, requiring careful preparations and memorising our scripts. We were not allowed to show live an actual neurosurgical operation; we just included part of one of our films on a head injury patient with an intracranial haematoma (a clot of blood).

Some people, indeed including some senior medical doctors, on hearing about the programme in 1958 said that it could be dangerous for the public: some might faint sitting in front of their television sets!

On 'the day', initially there was a private test run with the BBC in London. Then that evening came the actual live broadcast; the producer had taken away all our scripts! We became anxious. However all went well.

Since then, of course, as we all know, there are numerous professionally made medical TV programmes; it appears that they are very carefully, expertly prerecorded and edited. Anything is permissible, including seeing babies being born, and many instances of dramatic medical and surgical emergencies with, quite often, emergency resuscitation from some injury or disease, because of cardio-respiratory failure. A different world! No doubt that some of these programmes, if carefully chosen and produced, may help to educate the public in certain medical matters. The programmes have become 'visual drama'.

The best of the television series, and I mean *real* medicine or surgery, are quite excellent, very professional, beautifully filmed and edited. What a difference to our black and white early, and non-edited, programme!

I need to be very careful if I am interviewed by 'the press' in an overseas country. On two occasions I was badly misquoted; both pertained to our National Health Service. My words were taken out of context in the newspapers, but my hosts, senior neurosurgeons, said it was most unfortunate, but it would be best to take no action (complicated and possibly expensive!).

I have been on the radio, and on television in other countries, always being careful of the nature and authenticity of the programme. I remember in a radio interview about almost an epidemic of some motor cyclists causing serious accidents; I used the term 'murder cycles'.

The Scottish Trust for the Physically Disabled (STPD) and the Margaret Blackwood Housing Association (MBHA)

Early in 1972 I received a telephone call in my office in the Department of Surgical Neurology in the Western General Hospital in Edinburgh. A cultured military sounding voice said he was Sir Bernard Fergusson, and he would like to have a talk with me. He came the same afternoon, a tall erect military figure, moustached, with a monocle. My name had been recommended by Sir John Bruce, Regius Professor of Surgery, the University of Edinburgh, to Sir Bernard.

Sir Bernard explained his plan, to institute and develop an organisation, a Trust for Physically Disabled Scottish people, and along with this, to establish a Housing Association.

Subsequently, Sir Bernard and Lady Fergusson, Mr John Macphail, Sir Michael Herries, Mr Alan Baxter, Mr James Whitton, Mr David Butter, Dr Robert Pringle and I formed the nucleus for the Trust, meeting in the Board Room of the North British Distillery where Mr Macphail was the Director, and at the end of a meeting, sampling the 'wares'. Early on, Dr Margaret Blackwood joined the group, and in 1972 the MBHA was founded. That lady, wheelchair bound because of her motor neurone disease, was a remarkable person, who had already, personally, achieved wonderful positive actions for physically disabled people.

Sir Bernard, subsequently having the title Brigadier, the Lord Ballantrae, who had been Governor General of New Zealand and who was the Hon. Colonel of the Black Watch, was a superb organiser, and the activities of both the STPD and the MBHA rapidly bore fruit, and went from strength to strength.

The STPD is a Charitable Trust, which established the MBHA, and has a wider remit than the MBHA. It is not a service provider, but is a founder of other organisations and of other related activities. I continue to be a trustee of both the STPD and the MBHA.

The MBHA, founded in 1972, is very active indeed. The aim is to break new ground in the design and management of high quality accessible housing, and to seek continual improvements, and also to work with and to influence others, beyond the MBHA organisation. Particular skills have been developed in designing and managing accessible housing.

Before the 1970s, many disabled people in Scotland, without wealthy parents, lived in institutions, lacking privacy and deprived of most of the basic essential freedoms of life.

The MBHA is superbly active and enterprising, pioneering and developing new types of accommodation throughout the mainland of Scotland, with excellent, caring staff. In addition to these provisions, recently, some additional specialised services have been developed by the MBHA, offering welfare rights advice, and advice on individual house purchasing, setting up a consultancy to meet a widely recognised shortage of access design expertise. Indeed it has a level of expertise that few can match.

The MBHA is a non-profit making registered charity.

CHAPTER 6

Examinations and examiners

A N EXAMINER OF MEDICAL DOCTORS requires knowledge, experience and competence. Quality assurance, fairness and non-discrimination are essential. Audits of examiners' performances are desirable.

There may be 'hawks' and 'doves', as shown by careful monitoring of actual examinations. I saw this when I was involved with the examinations of overseas doctors (the Temporary Registration Assessment Board – TRAB and the Professional and Linguistics Assessment Board – PLAB tests); I was chairman of the executive committee, and we spoke personally to examiners who were consistently too tough (hawks), and to the doves, who were being too lenient. We were soon able to obtain definite, reasonable, improvements. Some students do not prepare themselves properly when undergoing written and oral examinations, reading and working up to the actual time of the tests. They become tired and flustered. I remember when I was invigilating in a written examination for the FRCSE, noticeably, one candidate had not started to write even although more than thirty minutes had passed. I asked if anything was wrong, and was told that he found it difficult to think and to gather his thoughts. He had been taking a Benzedrine-like stimulant drug to keep awake to work during the nights. It was necessary to get someone to accompany him back to where he was staying.

Once when I was in the USA I went to see the distinguished neurosurgeon Dr James Poppen in the Lahey Clinic. He was probably, in his time, the best technical neurosurgeon that I have ever seen: quick and beautiful – a master surgeon. At the conclusion of a long surgical list of a variety of neurosurgical conditions, we went into his office for coffee. There was a large pile of X-rays on his desk, and a viewing box. I was shown and was quizzed on each film. Some of the conditions were unusual, some very rare, but I did my best, and with a chuckle, studying the final X-ray, Dr Poppen said, 'You have just passed part of the USA Board of Neurosurgery!' Dr Poppen's book, an *Atlas of Neurosurgical Techniques* (1960), remains a classic.

Another memorable oral (viva voce) examination was in the neurology part of the MRCPE. My co-examiner was the famous neurologist and

98

philosopher Lord Brain. He could have asked some difficult questions, but in fact was kind and benign, although he expected good answers. During my turn to examine, and between candidates appearing, Lord Brain was making some interesting doodles on sheets of paper, Picasso-like. Interesting! We chatted, including his telling me about his favourite TV programme, which was *Candid Camera*, rather to my surprise. A lecture by Lord Brain that I particularly like (in print in 1959) is his Arthur Stanley Eddington Memorial Lecture: 'Science, Philosophy and Religion'.

Member of examination boards

RCSE General Fellowship in Surgery. Diplomas in Ophthalmology and in Dental Surgery.
Fellowship in Otolaryngology.
RCPE Membership.
RCP and S Glas Fellowship in Surgery.
Diploma in Psychological Medicine of the Scottish Royal Colleges.
Temporary Registration Assessments Board, and the Professional and Language Assessments Board. (TRAB and PLAB).

Examinations for overseas doctors

It was decided in Britain that a test should be considered, designed and organised on behalf of the British General Medical Council, for overseas doctors seeking post-graduate training in the UK, under temporary registration. A working party of representatives of the Royal Medical Colleges and the Society of Apothecaries met in London on 1 July 1974. I was a member of this working party and of the Temporary Registration Assessments Board (TRAB), which was established in July 1975, and I was Chairman from 1979 to 1987. The name of the test was changed to the Professional and Linguistics Assessment Board (PLAB).

The test had two components: (a) Proficiency in the English Language (tapes, written English and a viva); and (b) Professional knowledge MCQ; MSA (medical short answer paper, and a viva). Diets were held in Edinburgh (including the first test), Glasgow and London. All of us planning these tests sat one (we did quite well!). In one, surely apocryphal, story: in a MSA paper was the question: 'Briefly, mention possible ways to prevent peptic ulcer formation.' Answer: 'No hurry, no worry, no curry'! Early on, one aspect of the tests concerned us. We carefully noted and assessed the scoring of the tests by the several medical and language examiners, and found that there was a small but important number of 'doves' – who were being really too lenient, and also a small number of 'hawks' – who were regularly giving low marks, compared to their co-examiners. Personal talks with both types had the effect that we desired.

One candidate did very well in the written parts of the tests, but he had a bad stutter; and this was bit of a problem for the spoken, viva parts of the test. This was overcome by asking him to chant, or even sing his answers (stutterers can chant or sing normally): he passed.

PLAB is a major, important medical examination in the UK, thus in 2004, 12,588 overseas doctors sat part 1 and 8,214 part 2; these candidates became eligible to apply for Limited Registration with the General Medical Council (GMC). These numbers are large; UK medical schools continue to produce about 4,500 graduates in a year. (Information was kindly provided by the GMC.)

CHAPTER 7

Miscellany

A S I GATHERED MATERIAL for this book, some items did not readily fit into the six chapters as have been set out. Unfortunately I have never kept a diary, but I jot down 'memories', relying on the somewhat rusty temporal lobes (for memory) of my brain. These various miscellaneous items are now gathered together as Chapter Seven's Miscellany.

Indeed, as I write this, another small memory surfaces. In the operating theatres in our Department, included in the sterile instruments and equipment for our operations were sterilised blank drawing sheets and pencils to enable the surgeon, if desired, to make sketches of aspects of the operation being undertaken. These were retained in the patient's case records, reminding the surgeon later, when he was writing up the operation notes. Such drawings were useful also for teaching and research purposes. For any special neurosurgical procedures, we made an arrangement to call in, indeed into the operating theatre, Mr Clifford Shepley, the University of Edinburgh medical artist. His professional drawings were subsequently available for likely publications. Of course we also had photographic records, and indeed later, television facilities available.

The Norman M. Dott Memorial Trust

On his retiral, I decided that it would be appropriate to commemorate this distinguished surgeon in a practical way, and formed the Dott Memorial Trust, which I chaired, with Dr W. S. Watson as secretary. We collected monies and opened a bank account. The plans were to invite illustrious clinical neuroscientists to give an annual Normal Dott lecture, also to present a special medal annually to the best candidate taking the Intercollegiate Specialty Examination in Neurosurgery. In their book on Dott, Rush and Shaw state that they received a generous donation from the N.M. Dott Memorial Trust towards the initial expenses of the book.

Professor Dott's Personal Medical Library

Sheelagh telephoned me to my office one morning, to inform me that all of Norman Dott's books were being auctioned. I went to the auction forthwith and was successful in my bid for the books, against my friend, Dr Clifford Mawdsley, Consultant Neurologist. There were many volumes, filling what little available space I had in my study, and overflowing into our garage!

Invitations from publishers

Twice I was approached by publishers regarding two important text-books, inviting me to edit new editions of them:

(a) Northfield's *Surgery of the Central Nervous System* (Blackwell Scientific Publications, Edinburgh/Oxford): and
(b) Sir Ludwig Guttmann's *Spinal Cord Injuries* (Blackwell Scientific Publications, Edinburgh/Oxford).

However I had to decline, although I was greatly honoured to be invited. At the time I was extremely busy as a neurosurgeon, seeing and operating on patients, teaching, involved with my researches and other writings, and busy as editor of *Spinal Cord*. I felt that I was unable to give the necessary attention that was essential for these important endeavours.

What if?

What if Norman Dott had not had that motor cycle accident, fracturing his leg; being admitted to Edinburgh Royal Infirmary, and being intrigued and impressed with his treatment and the various activities in the hospital, so much so that he subsequently switched from the University Engineering faculty to the Medical faculty. He probably would have become a distinguished, inventive engineer, instead of a neurosurgeon.

Then, what if Ludwig Guttmann, and his family had not been persecuted by the Nazis in Germany because of the disgusting anti-semitism, and been forced to emigrate to England. My guess is that he would have become a leader of European neurosurgery.

Professor J. Douglas Miller (1937–95)

We were very fortunate in attracting Professor J. Douglas Miller to our Department.

Douglas was a very good clinician, and a distinguished neuroscientist. His researches included studies of cerebrospinal fluid, intracranial pressure, and cerebral blood flow. Unfortunately he had an untimely death.

A lunch party

Sheelagh and I were invited to a very pleasant, private, lunch party, where the guests included Madame Valentina Tereshkova, the first lady Russian cosmonaut, and her charming daughter, who is a neurosurgeon in Moscow. We had excellent conversations, in English.

Dr Charles Drake and his wife Ruth

He was a superb neurosurgeon, specialising in the treatment of very difficult cerebral aneurysms – and receiving patients from many countries. He was Chief of the Department of Neurosurgery in London, Ontario, Canada. I watched him operate on extremely complex aneurysms, cursing away as was his wont. He had a large library containing unedited video tapes of his many operations. Charles and Ruth were wonderful hosts. They flew us, Sheelagh, our daughter Frances and me, up to his vacation home at Lion's Head. An expert pilot, Charles's air flights included piloting Canadian Service jets. Charles was also a key person internationally in neurosurgery; and a President of the World Federation of Neurosurgical Societies.

The Clowards

Dr Ralph Cloward, a distinguished neurosurgeon from Hawaii with his wife and son visited us in Edinburgh. They, along with Sheelagh and me, had lunch with Professor and Mrs Dott. Later, I had made arrangements, obtaining tickets, to witness the opening of the wonderful new Forth Road Bridge by Her Majesty the Queen, when there would be a fly-past of RAF aeroplanes, and also as part of the ceremony, several Royal Naval ships would be present in the river Forth. However a dense fog rapidly came in and blotted out everything – no planes, no ships and no visible bridge! But we could hear some music and of course we could see Her Majesty. Later I managed to obtain tickets for the Clowards for a film of the construction of the bridge, which was being shown in the Usher Hall in Edinburgh.

Mr John Shaw

John was my esteemed collegue for several years. He specialised in paediatric neurosurgery.

The Mayfields and the McLaurins in Cincinnati, USA

We stayed with Dr Frank Mayfield and Queenie, his charming wife. They were excellent hosts. We had previously met them at a lovely lunch party in Norman Dott's home. Dr Mayfield was a neurosurgeon of international fame, and an important inventor, in particular of the Mayfield aneurysm clips, and of the Mayfield head clamp, items used universally by neurosurgeons. I gave lectures and did ward rounds.

Also in Cincinnati are our close friends Professor Robert McLaurin, a notable paediatric neurosurgeon, and his wife, Cathy. We see each other at intervals over the years. He is a quite delightful person, and a great golfing partner.

Dr and Mrs W. J. Gardner

In Cleveland, Ohio (at the famous clinic there), Sheelagh and I were generously hosted by the Gardners. He was a clever, innovative neuro-surgeon, and a somewhat demanding but very friendly chief. For example on one special anniversary his staff presented him with a beautiful gun; he enjoyed shooting as a pasttime. The unusual thing about the rifle was that the barrel had been machine bent, so that someone using it would, in theory at least, shoot himself! Dr Gardner got the message and had the gun fixed to the wall above his sitting-room fireplace. Neurosurgeons will know Dr Gardener as an ideas man. As just one example: Gardner-Wells skull tongs are used universally.

Professor Earl A. Walker, his wife Agnes, and the Udvarheylis

We were hosted in Baltimore, USA, by Professor Walker, one of the keenest, most erudite, academic American neurosurgeons, steeped in the neurosciences, including basic research on epilepsy. He was a key international figure, Chief of Neurosurgery in the famous John Hopkins University and medical school, where modern neurosurgery really started.

On his staff was a very old friend of Sheelagh and myself, Dr George Udvarheyli. He trained in our department in Edinburgh, and indeed married our lovely speech therapist, Elspeth, a Scottish Highland lass. They are a highly cultured pair, much involved in the arts. Indeed, I sometimes thought that he would have been happy as an orchestra conductor. Sheelagh and I had a great time, including attending a New Year Ball in fancy dress. All four of us went as 'the Hungarian String Quartet', wearing string vests and carrying cardboard shaped instruments.

Who are the mentors' mentors?

This in itself is an interesting study. A few examples are:

- Harvey Cushing: Osler and Halstead.
- Wilder Penfield: Sherrington and Foerster.
- Norman Dott: Sharpey-Schaeffer and Cushing.
- Ludwig Guttmann: Foerster.

Sir Ludwig Guttmann (1899–1980)

His father was an innkeeper and distiller. He became an orderly in a local accident hospital, and one day saw a miner who had broken his back. He witnessed the (apparent) reduction of the spinal deformity by extension and direct pressure, as had been recommended very many years ago by Galen. Ludwig was told by the doctors that the man would be dead in a few weeks but he thought this to be a defeatist attitude. The case deeply impressed him. Because of a throat abscess, requiring drainage, when Ludwig was called up for Army service in 1917, the drainage tube was still required, and he was rejected for military service. He began his medical studies in Breslau.

Neurological disturbances of intestinal function

(Note: This item really is only for those with medical training).

Several important abnormalities of intestinal function may result from certain disturbances, usually acute from trauma of the central or of the autonomic parts of the nervous system. I will only cite two examples of many conditions that I have encountered:

- After an acute spinal cord injury, paralytic ileus may develop, and must be recognised and be promptly treated. (That is, where part of the small bowel (intestine) has become paralysed, and thus it is obstructed.)
- A head injury patient developed acute intestinal obstruction, and was very ill. Assistance from a general surgeon was obtained. The emergency laparotomy revealed an unusual pathology of the small intestine. There were five retrograde intussusceptions of the small bowel, but fortunately no evidence of gangrene.

Treatment was quite satisfactory. (Intussusception is the inversion (or invagination) of one portion of the intestine and its reception within an adjacent portion). My patient actually had five such invaginations, and they were all retrogrades.

Tuberculosis

When I was a young doctor, and then a neurosurgeon in training, tuberculosis was rife. There were notices in the Edinburgh streets warning people that 'Spitting Spreads Disease'. There were special hospital facilities for people of all ages with some of the many forms of tuberculosis, including the lungs, bones and joints, meningitis (the meninges are the coverings of the brain and spinal cord) and brain (cerebral) tuberculomas. Indeed, no part of the body was immune. An important children's hospital in Edinburgh was the Princess Margaret Rose, in Fairmilehead (by the way, our Rotary Club gathered large sums of monies towards its initial construction) which was for two main conditions – tuberculosis, and anterior poliomyelitis.

Throughout the history of man, tuberculosis has been a major scourge, causing innumerable deaths and much misery. There was no real curative treatment: rest, fresh air, a good diet, possibly isolation; surgical treatment was necessary for certain tuberculous lesions. I would refer the reader to the wonderful book, *The Magic Mountain*, by the Nobel prizewinner Thomas Mann. But 'a magic bullet' did become available. This was from a brilliant medical researcher, Selman Waksman, whose family came from Russia but as Jews were persecuted they therefore emigrated to the USA. His vital work resulted in the discovery in 1943 of streptomycin. His researches are fully given in the *Historical Review*, the British Journal of Diseases of the Chest, 1988, 82: 23–31, Selman Waksman (1888–1975). It is an enthralling story which I feel would most likely interest both medical and lay people. Research studies in animals were absolutely essential; also indeed, two doctors in the Mayo Clinic in the USA injected themselves with tubercle bacteria, as guinea-pigs, to help to prove the case. The drug was really 'a miracle', and revolutionised the treatment of tuberculosis. Waksman received numerous honours, the main one being the Nobel Prize for Medicine.

Spot the Ball

In Britain, a popular newspaper competition is to 'Spot the Ball'. There is a photograph of a football (soccer) game, with the ball missing from the photo. The problem for competitors is to place a mark where they think the ball was (there could be many hundreds of possibilities). The chance of correctly locating the ball is really remote, but the editor will accept the nearest place. However one elderly gentleman from the north of Scotland identified the correct ball location on a number of occasions. The editor was intrigued, and he sent a reporter up to interview this gentleman, and ask how he was so successful. The gentleman said that he was a retired academic, and did things 'scientifically'. He had won enough money. Therefore he now demonstrated what he did. Shutting his eyes, he took a pin and stabbed the spot the ball photo, several times, until he heard 'plop and hiss' – that was the ball! This amusing story was told at an Edinburgh University dinner which I attended, by (the late) Sir Edward Appleton, distinguished scientist, and Principal of the University.

Playing chicken

I remember two vivid examples of the 'game' known as 'playing chicken'.

The first was in the dark in a disused former railway line cutting; two youths on motor cycles faced each other many yards apart, headlamps on. They accelerated, racing towards each other. The 'game' was not to give way until the very last moment. However one of the youths died instantly from the collision, and the other was rushed to our department, with a major head-brain injury.

The other took place on a visit to a hospital in a hill station in North America. I gave some lectures, and Sheelagh and I were shown around the hospital, which was modern and well staffed and equipped. In a male ward there were several men with one or both legs missing. At dinner that evening I mentioned this unusual appearance to the hospital director, who explained that the men got paid once a month and some celebrated by drinking a good deal of alcohol; and sometimes a few of the workers played 'chicken', by placing their legs across a nearby railway line, hopefully to remove them just in time as a train came along!

The Alabama National Guard

When Governor Wallace of Alabama was shot, the bullet wound passed through his spine, rendering him paraplegic, permanently. However he received excellent treatment in a spinal injuries centre, and in recognition of this he decided to communicate with doctors who were council members of medical organisations concerned with spinal cord injury patients, and offer them the honour of being an 'honorary Colonel in the Alabama National Guard'. I did not accept this, but sure enough, a handsome document was mailed to me proclaiming that I was now an honorary Colonel.

A hot party

During our stay with the Greenwoods in Houston, Texas, the famous cardiac surgeon Dr Michael DeBakey put on a dinner party for us. Lovely, up to a point, but this was our first (and last!) experience of real Mexican food. It took us almost two days to fully recover!

Professor Sir James Learmonth

He was a Scot, born in 1895. His father was a schoolteacher. He served for six years with the King's Own Scottish Borders in World War I. Then he graduated in medicine in Glasgow. He obtained a Rockefeller Fellowship (like Dott), which took him to the USA, studying neurosurgery in the Mayo Clinic. He became the Regius Professor of Surgery in Edinburgh. His main interests were anatomical, physiological on clinical aspects of disorders of the peripheral and of the autonomic nerves. He was a Visiting Professor of Surgery in Harvard University, and in the Peter Bent Brigham hospital in Boston. He introduced the excellent Saturday morning surgical meetings in Edinburgh, rotating through each specialty; also 'the deaders', confidential details of each death occurring in the previous interval of the meeting of a specialty, for full discussion. In addition, a young member of the surgical specialty's team was required to read an original medical paper or present an interesting case which was then freely commented on by Sir James and the other surgeons present. This was the only situation in my experience of being taught some of the aspects of being a satisfactory teacher. As University lecturers and senior lecturers we did not routinely receive any real guidance.

Some of our medical school, undergraduate and postgraduate teachers were quite good, a few were very good, and some were average. The best became role models. I think that students, at least some of them, can be quite good judges of the real teaching abilities of their lecturers, noting delivery, content, clarity of presentation, and making everything really interesting, even at times fascinating and memorable, and with meaningful visual aids.

A neophyte speaker

A young overseas neurosurgeon who had probably never previously read a scientific paper before a large international conference, went on and on, ignoring the green light on the podium changing to yellow, then to red –

which meant 'stop now!' But he also ignored the chairman's message on a slip of paper telling him to stop. The problem was resolved when two members from the audience of neurosurgeons went on to the stage and lifted the speaker off – but he was still reading his paper out loud!

If coloured lights don't work, I have a simple remedy: playing a bit of loud but good Scottish bagpipe music on a tape!

The Salmon Report

When I was chairman of the Medical and Dental Staff Committee of the Royal Infirmary of Edinburgh, one day, Miss Nimmo, the matron, asked if she could please speak to the staff about the new Salmon Report. I agreed. (Mr Salmon was one of the senior directors of Marks and Spencer.) We were told about forthcoming changes in the seniority, titles and work of senior nurses. But the medical and dental staff were not too pleased about the likely changes, which would aim to give some senior (clinical) nursing sisters a higher grade and salary, but at the expense of discontinuing clinical work. Certainly my own senior ward sister, Miss Rhoda Kerr, had no intention of becoming a 'clip-board' nursing administrator. She remained as my excellent senior ward sister. I was delighted!

What will you do?

We had groups of final year medical students attached to our department for a week, and at the end of their last day there was a tea-party in Sister's sitting room. I chatted with several, and asked one, a tall, well built young man, who could possibly have become a Scottish rugby team player, what he would like to do in medicine after qualifying. His answer surprised me: 'I enjoyed orthopaedic surgery, Sir, but as I get older I may find the long hours and the physical requirements of such a surgeon too much. I will see!' I was taken aback; certainly, not for a moment had I ever worried about possible (but they were certain!) long arduous hours, and often also nights of a neurosurgeon!

A variety show experience

When I was a young doctor I invited a pretty young lady to accompany me to go to the King's Theatre in Edinburgh for the Half-Past Eight Variety Show. There was a good deal of laughter during the show watching the antics of the Scottish comedians. I noticed that my friend at times appeared to be sleeping. I guessed that she was tired from working long hours. Then, at times she was fully awake. It gradually dawned on me that she most probably had a form of narcolepsy, where the individual reacts by lightly sleeping when experiencing strong emotions. I was too embarrassed to ask her questions, in particular if she was on medication.

An Egyptian experience

Our good friend, General Sayed El Gindi, an Egyptian neurosurgeon, invited us to Cairo, where I would be the Visiting Neurosurgeon and Specialist Lecturer. I went, and did some teaching, and examined a number of patients in the Neurosurgical Department of the Mahadi Military Hospital in Cairo, and carried out several major neurosurgical operations, cerebral and spinal, including one patient with a 'tricky' cerebral aneurysm. All went well. The facilities were excellent in that hospital. The social aspects of our stay were also very pleasant.

A golfing partner

I greatly enjoy some gentle golf, two or three times a week, at my course in Edinburgh, the Bruntsfield Links Golfing Society (BLGS), founded in 1761. I usually play with my good friend Drew (Andrew) Turnbull. Like myself, he is not too young!, but he is as 'bright as a button' (an odd term!), with a full reservoir of interesting memories. He is always beautifully turned out. One of his favourite remarks is: 'Our golf requires some fine tuning!'

On being observed

A well known surgeon, who was in great demand as a visiting lecturer, participating in several UK and overseas medical centres, was therefore away from Edinburgh quite a lot. On returning to Edinburgh after one of these visits, he found this little printed notice stuck to the windscreen of his car: 'Visitor to Britain'!

Fund raising

Many of us have on occasion sought funds for a worthwhile charitable cause, but be careful! There is the tale of the junior schoolteacher, who at the end of term asked her young pupils, if possible, to bring something interesting for the annual school charity event to raise money. Next day, Jimmy arrived carrying an oxygen tent. The teacher was surprised. She

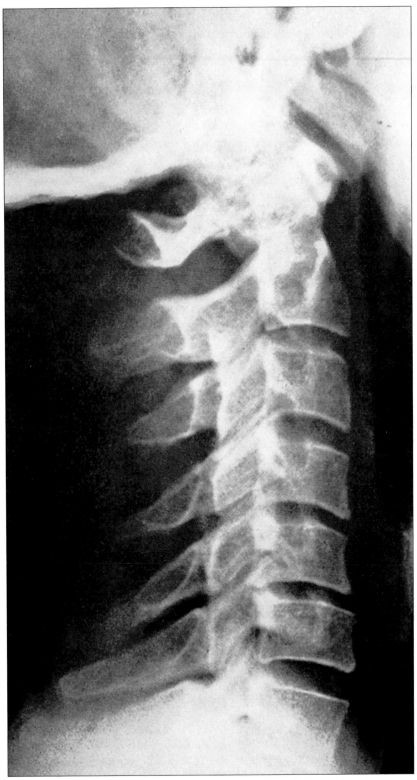

33. *Lateral X-Ray of the cervical spine: severe cervical spondylosis at C (cervical) 4–5 and C5–6 levels, with degenerate narrowed discs, posterior osteophytes (bone lipping at these levels), and narrowing (stenosis) of the spinal canal.*
Courtesy of Nature Publishing Group, London

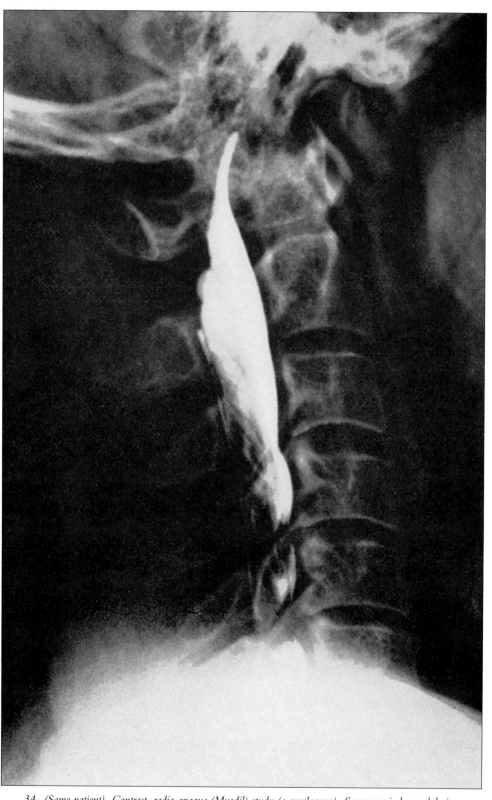

34. (Same patient). Contrast, radio-opaque (Myodil) study (a myelogram). Severe cervical spondylosis seen.
Courtesy of Nature Publishing Group, London

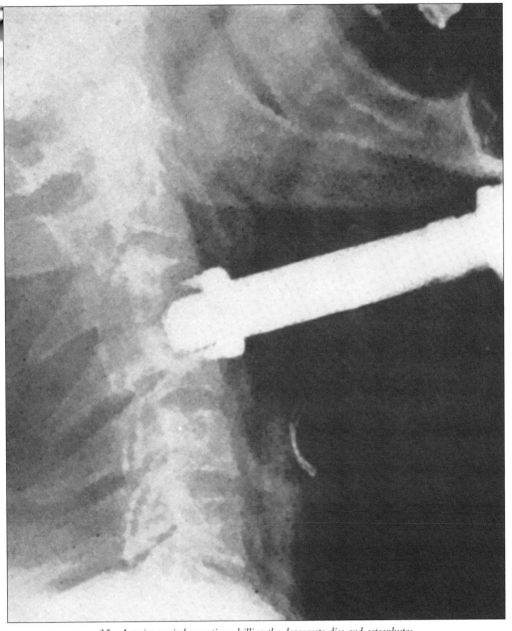

35. Anterior cervical operation: drilling the degenerate disc and osteophytes.
Courtesy of Nature Publishing Group, London

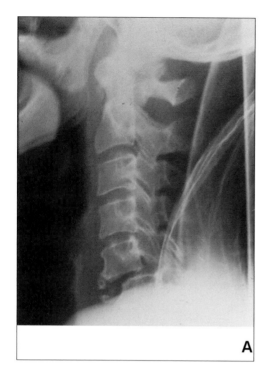

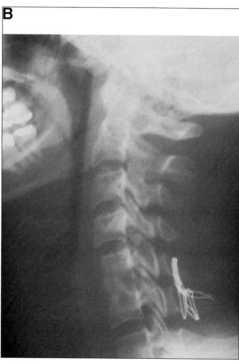

36. Radiographs showing a fracture-dislocation (a slipping forwards of C5 vertebra on C6 vertebra) of the cervical spine. A before treatment. B after treatment

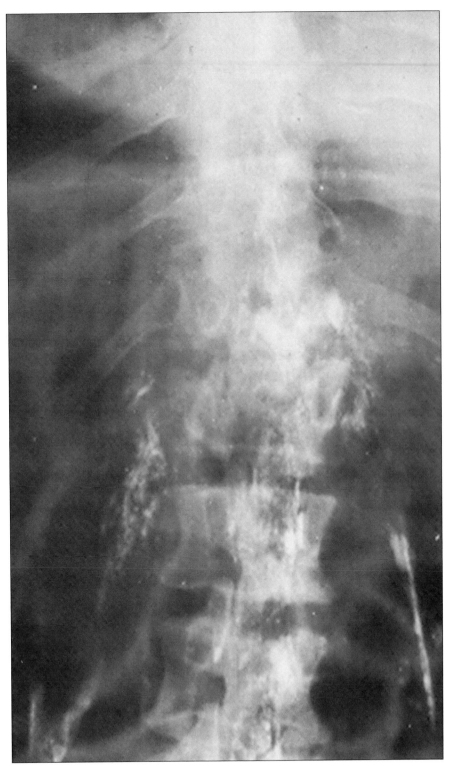

37. *Myelogram (injection of radio-opaque Myodil into the spinal subarachnoid space) showing the fracture-dislocation of the lumbar spine, with some of the Myodil streaming out of tears in the arachnoid and dura covering the lumbar and sacral nerve roots (the cauda equina), into the paravertebral lumbar region. At operation, several of these nerve roots had prolapsed through the tears; they were replaced, and then the arachnoid and dural tears were sutured and closed*

38. *Sir Ludwig Guttmann*

39. *Paralympic Games: wheelchair racing.* Courtesy of Richard Brickley, Scottish Disability Sport

40. *Royal College of Surgeons of Edinburgh. Symposium on Spinal Cord Injuries, June 1963. (left to right in the photograph) Front: David Band (Urological Surgeon); Hank Verbiest (Dutch Neurosurgeon); Sir Walter Mercer (Orthopaedic Surgeon); Sir Ludwig Guttmann; J. J. Mason Brown (Paediatric Surgeon, College President); Ernest Bors (USA, Spinal Injury Consultant); Norman Dott; J. Cosbie Ross (Urological Surgeon); A. B. Rossier (Switzerland, Spinal Injury Consultant). Middle: Marek Damanski (Spinal Injury Consultant); J. W. McLeod (Bacteriologist); A. C. Buchan (Plastic Surgeon); myself; F. W. Holdsworth (Orthopaedic Surgeon); R. C. Schneider (USA, Neurosurgeon); A. F. J. Maloney (Neuropathologist); A. L. Naughton (Clinical Neuropsychologist); W. G. Kerr (General Surgeon); J. Newsam (Urological Surgeon); J. A. Simpson (Neurologist and Clinical Neurophysiologist); Inset: G. J. Romanes (Neuro-anatomist); J. A. Ross (General Surgeon)*

41. *Sheelagh and I visiting the wonderful Taj Mahal, India*

asked how Jimmy got the item. He said, 'From my uncle, Miss.' And what, she asked, did he say? 'Help, Help!'

Pre-empting the NHS?

It was 4.30 p.m. on the operating theatre clock. Mr John ('Jock') Struthers, general surgeon in the Royal Infirmary of Edinburgh, was mid-way through a major abdominal operation. He stood back, removed his gloves and went out of the theatre. Everyone, including the attendant medical students of which I was one, was perplexed, but we soon realised what was happening. The chief, Mr Struthers was concerned about the pending inception of the 'new medical era', the National Health Service (NHS), probably requiring him to 'clock in and clock out'. He reckoned that he had done his fixed hours of work that day! The message was clear. However, having made the gesture, Jock Struthers scrubbed up again and completed the operation!

A hirsute problem

When I was a trainee with Professor Dott, a new registrar came to the department to start work, but he had grown a quite magnificent beard. This did not appeal to the chief who told the doctor to remove the beard. He complied, and the now smooth-faced young man began his neurosurgical training!

I remember well my own 'hirsute' problem, returning home from a leave in the RAMC with a moustache, of which I was rather proud. However my mother thought otherwise: it doesn't suit! To make peace, I shaved it off.

First aid

Whilst dining in our Club in Edinburgh, a young lady at another table suddenly rose up, choking, and rushed out of the room. I followed right away, indeed to the ladies room, and immediately applied the Heimlich manoeuvre, and a plug of undigested meat popped out of her mouth, from her throat. There was immediate great relief!

Another incident took place on vacation in Majorca. From the pool-side, I saw a young girl lying still on the bottom of the pool, probably drowning. There were very few people about, and although not much of a swimmer, I dived in, and brought the child out, indeed pulling on her long hair. She was pale, cold, had poor pulses and was not breathing. Immediate routine resuscitative measures were most fortunately successful – she rallied, and recovered.

During mid-Atlantic flights, on two separate occasions, there was an urgent call for the help of a doctor, but no one went forward. Therefore, I did, explaining that I was a doctor, but a neurosurgeon. The patient was having an acute asthmatic attack. Fortunately there was oxygen, and the patient had appropriate medications in her hand luggage for such emergency. All went well.

On the other occasion, a hospital theatre nurse was certain that she had acute appendicitis. But my history and clinical examination showed that she had acute gastroenteritis.

Once, in a cinema, the film stopped, the lights went on, and the manager came on to the stage, seeking a doctor urgently. No one got up, therefore I went forward to the manager's office, where I found a young woman, very pale and shocked, who was bleeding vaginally. She was rushed to hospital.

I should explain that my name is 'Mr', not 'Dr' Harris. I am therefore not known in aircraft or hotels as a medical doctor, but if someone has an urgent medical condition and no medical doctor goes forward, I will then explain myself and try to help. There can be some problems, medical/professional and medical/legal, for a medical doctor taking on the responsibility of an unknown patient's illness or injury, especially outside one's own country.

Attempted suicide

In all my many years as a junior doctor, and subsequently a neurosurgical consultant in Edinburgh, I only encountered one civilian patient with a neurological gun-shot wound. Very depressed, he shot himself but was not good at using a pistol and only managed superficial damage to his head and quite minimal cerebral damage. He had neurosurgical and psychiatric care.

Jumping off certain Edinburgh bridges appeals to some people wanting to end their lives, but when attempting this they do not, apparently wish to risk, when conscious, having any pain. A row of small sharp metal spikes on the parapet of bridges therefore appears to deter an attempted suicide person. But one young very depressed individual jumped off an ordinary bridge, landing on an elderly gentleman below, who was instantly killed. The depressed person came under my care in our department. There were serious multiple injuries, brain, spinal and pelvis; with urgent appropriate treatment she survived but had residual physical and intellectual problems.

Another person, who was very depressed, jumped from a high up window where she lived and sustained a compound fracture of the lumbar spine with a partial lesion of the lower (lumbar and sacral) spinal nerve roots. Imaging studies revealed a tear in the dura and arachnoid theca (the layers of tissue covering the spinal cord and nerve roots). There was prolapse of the nerve roots through the tear. At operation they were replaced in their normal anatomical location and the dura was closed. The damaged spine was stable, therefore no special metallic or other type of fixation was required. She made a full neurological recovery. (Note – if such prolapsed nerves are not replaced within the dura and arachnoid they will become adherent to each other and to the adjacent tissues with an increasing neurological deficit, which will probably be permanent.

Unacceptable terms and words

I do not favour the term that a person is 'a paraplegic'. We should say that that a person 'has paraplegia'. If such an individual also happens to have diabetes, that person should not be known as a 'paraplegic diabetic', but that he or she 'has paraplegia and diabetes'.

I dislike the term 'brain surgeon', when what is usually meant is a 'neurosurgeon'. Such a specialist as has already been mentioned in the Preface of this book is a medical doctor specially trained to have a detailed knowledge of the nervous system, the brain, head, spine, spinal cord and nerves, so that diseases or injuries of the nervous system can be diagnosed, and if and when indicated, treated by a neurosurgical operation.

The prevention of diseases and injuries to the nervous system

To do justice to the very important topic of the prevention, primary or secondary, of many neurological diseases and injuries, would necessitate an appreciable enlargement of parts of this book. Some pointers have been included in the earlier chapters. Certainly every neurosurgeon must be fully familiar with all that comes under the heading of 'Prevention'.

I will just briefly mention one personal experience that I well remember.

I was invited down to a car manufacturer in Coventry, to give a lecture and take part in discussions on the prevention of head and spinal injuries in car accidents. My visit included a remarkable ride in their new Range

Rover, over their almost impossible rather frightening special very bumpy 'road' which also had several sharp bends. Quite an experience!

An epidemic of ageing

As predicted by the United Nations (2000 revision), there is an epidemic of ageing impending in the Western world. The number of people aged over sixty years will triple from 606 million worldwide in 2000 to nearly 2 billion by 2050. There is expected to be a more than fivefold increase in those aged over eighty years, from 69 million in 2000 to 379 million by 2050. People aged over sixty years make up about 20 per cent of the population in more developed regions of the world; by 2050 they will probably account for 33 per cent.

The UK is predicted to have about 16 million people over the age of sixty years by 2040. There is likely to be some important serious, medical consequences including an increase and worsening of people with such conditions as degenerative vascular and degenerative skeletal disturbances, as consequences of the above significant demographic changes.

An unwelcome experience

When I was a senior neurosurgical registrar, one morning I received an official letter stating that too many British senior registrars were being trained in surgery. The authorities said that some should consider going into general practice, or becoming a medical officer in the Armed Forces, or work in an overseas country. Sheelagh and I were taken aback! We had young children at school, and a nice home in Edinburgh, and my hope was to become a consultant neurosurgeon. I did nothing. There was an outcry about the letter. I heard no more.

A tuneful ending

My good friend Dr John Stanton, Consultant neurologist, and I were both scheduled to read scientific papers in a Neurological Symposium in the Royal College of Physicians, Edinburgh. He told me that his secretary was away, and asked if my secretary, Miss Irene Pearson, could kindly type out his paper. This was arranged, but when my secretary came to the conclusion of Dr Stanton's paper, which was on tape, to her great surprise and amusement, the last two paragraphs were sung by Dr Stanton, in his deep, loud baritone voice!

CHAPTER 8

Two artistic giants

Van Gogh stated that 'one cannot look at a Rembrandt without believing in God.'

S INCE I WAS YOUNG I HAVE developed an interest in some aspects of the arts, in particular, painting and music. Here, I will just briefly allude to two of our – Sheelagh's and my – favourite artists, Rembrandt and Mahler.

Rembrandt and medicine

(An excerpt from my article with the same title, published in the *Journal of the Royal College of Surgeons of Edinburgh* (1995, 40, 81–83). Published here by permission from the College.)

Rembrandt Harmenszoon van Rijn, the famous painter, was born on 15 July 1606 in Leyden, Holland. He attended Leyden University and subsequently moved to Amsterdam. He married his beloved, beautiful Saskia. It has been said that to respond to the art of Rembrandt is one of the greatest experiences of mankind.

One's interest in this painter genius has increased over the years, in relation to his most wonderful paintings, etchings and drawings. Several of his works have medical connotations. He obviously had a considerable knowledge of history, the bible, mythology, social problems, philosophy and anatomy.

He became increasingly interested in reality and in the world of emotions, including the development of a specialised form of chiaroscuro. He was also a man of compassion, being very sympathetic to the poor, the weak and the outcast. An artistic genius, in addition to his wonderful paintings and drawings, he was the master etcher of all times. An artist genius, Rembrandt transformed the ugly, the pedestrian and the sacred into beauty, by rendering it in the simplest possible form.

There was a strong link to the Medical School of Leyden University, which was considered to be the most famous medical faculty in Europe in the seventeenth century, and scholars who were attracted there from many countries. Several came from Scotland. The first Scottish graduate of that University was Peter Coldman, who graduated in 1610. Eleven Edinburgh doctors who studied in Leyden were founders of the Royal College of Physicians of Edinburgh. Indeed, 102 Leyden trained medical doctors who came from Edinburgh became associated with that College. Scotland can also claim the credit of providing Archibald Pitcairn as Professor of Medicine in Leyden from 1692 to 1694; he had the great doctor Boerhaave among his pupils. John Rutherford, at Leyden in 1718, and an FRCPE in 1724, was the first Professor of Medicine in Edinburgh to give lectures, in 1725.

In 1741 he introduced clinical teaching in the Royal Infirmary of Edinburgh. He was the maternal grandfather of Sir Walter Scott.

Rembrandt himself was a popular and indeed very demanding teacher of painting and drawing with classes consisting of some thirty-five pupils with a three-year apprenticeship – but there were no degrees or diplomas at the end of the courses! He was a consummate anatomist. In the early seventeenth century surgery was taught in the University of Amsterdam in theory only, it being felt that practising surgery was beneath a doctor's dignity, although a good theoretical knowledge of anatomy was necessary to become a physician. Once a year the Anatomy Surgeons' Guild was granted the body of an executed criminal for dissection, and the City Council appointed an instructor in anatomy with the title of Praelector Anatomiae. Successful student candidates after four years' study could start a barber-surgeon's shop, but were required to attend theoretical lectures for no less than twenty years: postgraduate education!

Rembrandt's Dr Tulp painting has some resemblance to Vesalius' title page, where Vesalius is seen to be the centre of a crowd, dissecting and teaching.

Several of Rembrandt's works involve anatomy, physiology, medical topics and education. They include The Anatomy Lesson of Dr Tulp (1632); The Anatomy Lesson of Dr Joan Deyman (1655); Portrait of a Scholar; Dr Ephraim Bonus (1647); Two Scholars Disputing (1628); A Scholar in a Lofty Room; Scholar in a Room with a Winding Stair; Susannah and the Elders; The Circumcision (1626, 1630, and 1654); Christ Disputing with the Doctors; Bathsheba; Man Micturating; Woman Micturating; Dog Defaecating; Uzziah Stricken with Leprosy (1630); Christ Healing the Sick (1649).

In the famous painting, The Anatomy Lesson of Dr Nicholas Pieterzoon Tulp (1632) (Mauritshius, The Hague), Rembrandt had received a very important commission, which indeed at the early age of twenty-six established his reputation and fame and led to many more commissions. Dr Tulp was a well known physician and a distinguished anatomist, becoming known as 'Vesalius Redivivus', that is, Vesalius reformed. His textbook of medicine contains what was apparently the first description of beriberi. He had requested the building of the Anatomy Theatre in Amsterdam. In the painting, Dr Tulp is shown demonstrating the long flexor tendons in the left forearm of a cadaver, Adiaan Adiaansz, a boiler-maker who had been executed by hanging on 31 January 1632. He is being observed by Board Members of the Guild of Surgeon Anatomists of Amsterdam; indeed altogether some two or three hundred individuals would spectate at such a dissection. There is well known controversy about the accuracy of these long flexor tendons. Some anatomists and surgeons say that they are shown incorrectly, to be arising from the lateral epicondyle of the humerus. Thus Boake states that Rembrandt contrived a necessary error to show Dr Tulp holding up the structures in his forceps and the origin of the tendons 'if painted correctly' would have been hidden by the left upper abdomen. Wood Jones wrote that Rembrandt, although a wonderful anatomist, displayed the superficial flexor muscles of the fingers arising from the radial condyle of the humerus, and he appeared to have drawn the details of a right arm and then transposed them to the left arm. Mills after a visit to the Mauristius Collection at the Hague found that the master painter was absolutely right. He presumed that Wood Jones had not seen the original painting. Dr Tulp was retracting the superficial flexor muscles of the fingers laterally and it is clear that they are attached to the medial epicondyle of the humerus. Mills wondered if Wood Jones had seen the painting before it was cleaned, removing the heavy varnish covering. Comments on Mills' article included one from Romanes (Professor of Anatomy in Edinburgh), who felt that the origin of these long flexors was from the lateral epicondyle of the humerus: the pronator teres appeared to be passing from the lateral epicondyle towards the ulna on the medial side of the forearm. Small (surgeon), also commenting on Mills' article, said that the dissected limb in the cadaver did not appear to belong to it, for example, being longer than the right upper limb. But he felt that the anatomy was correct, the dissected specimen was rotated. Another point is that it was usual for a dissection to begin with the abdomen, which is intact in the painting. Brown said that the painting of the dissected arm could possibly have been made following a study of an anatomical illustration in Adriaen van den Spiegel's *Humane Corporis Fabrica*. However, the painting is a work of dynamic tension, showing the pallor of the cadaver, with Dr Tulp's hand raised depicting the use of the dissected tendons to flex the fingers, the light falling on the corpse and the fine portraits of the Board Members.

Indeed, hands play a very important part in the work of many artists, and certainly in the works of Rembrandt. There could be special significance of Dr Tulp's hands and the hand being dissected, a 'hand' to 'him that works manually'; a literal interpretation of the Greek word *cheirougos* (surgeon), which means just that – a surgeon being 'one who practises the art of healing by manual operation' (*Oxford English Dictionary*). In 1660, Rembrandt, aged fifty-four years, in a self-portrait, depicted his left hand (he was right-handed) as a 'prosthetic device' – a maul stick, palette and brushes – that is, the instrumental use of the hand. In his painting The Goldsmith (1665) he conjoined the two roles of the hands, loving and painting.

In his second 'Anatomy Lesson', The Anatomy Lesson of Dr Joan Deyman (1656), which was commissioned to honour the first dissection by the new head of the Medical School, the corpse was that of Joris Fonteyn, hanged for thievery, and is probably the first painting showing the human brain being dissected. Note that the abdomen had been dissected first. Unfortunately the painting was severely damaged by fire in 1723.

Referring again to 'hands', mention is made of these other Rembrandt works, in particular, A Woman in Bed; Bathsheba; The Jewish Bride, Jacob Blessing the Children of Joseph; The Return of the Prodigal Son; Aristotle Contemplating the Bust of Homer.

Rembrandt made some seventy self-portraits; indeed they form a remarkable autobiography of the painter. He was always realistic and honest; when young and affluent he would often depict himself wearing oriental or Venetian clothes. As he got older, he shows evidence of this, eventually illustrating the slow 'ruin of the flesh'; thus, for example, in his self-portrait in 1665, when he was aged fifty-nine years, he depicted himself as a contrast with a smile, as if to say '*Concedo nilli*' – 'I give in to nobody'. Why did he do so many self-portraits? Because he was the most readily available subject and could experiment with facial expressions, moods and emotions? A degree of introspection? A degree of narcissism? Certainly there must be some practical problem in carrying out self-portraits, such as the problem of 'a mirror image'.

Rembrandt was fascinated by religious themes, choosing themes that included striking visual effects and sensations; he was something of a mystic. Some of the important works are: The Raising of Lazarus; The Doubting of Thomas; The Apparition of Christ in the Garden; The Resurrection; The Blinding of Samson; The Sacrifice of Abraham; The Reconciliation of Absolom and David; Christ and the Samaritan; The Return of the Prodigal Son; Abraham and Ishmail; Jacob Blessing the Sons of Joseph; Saul in Disarrya before David; The Blind Tobit; The Blind Jacob Blessing his Grandson; Sarah awaiting Tobias on their Wedding Night; Belshazzar's Feast – The Writing on the Wall; The Jewish Bride. The last is a famous painting, 'a poignant depiction' of mature love, and it represents the biblical love story of Isaac and Rebecca (Genesis 26:8).

We have a remarkable man, an artistic genius. He was an innovator, a teacher, one who 'was his own man' and who never bowed to the imperators, nor to the demands of society. He could combine the supernatural and the real, the beautiful and the ugly. His portraits revealed character rather than mere likeness. He did not suffer fools gladly and could not tolerate hypocrisy: he quoted from the Bible: Ecclesiastes 1.2:

'Vanity of vanities, saith the Preacher, vanity of vanities: all is vanity. What profit had a man of all his labour which he taketh under the sun? One generation passeth away and another generation cometh.'

Gustav Mahler

Music has charms to sooth a savage breast
To soften rocks, or bend a knotted oak.

Congreve's Mourning Bride

One of the favourite composers of Sheelagh and myself is Gustav Mahler. His music, especially his nine symphonies, is wonderful, thought provoking and some is quite exciting. Each brings out, like a musical autobiography, many aspects of his fascinating but often tragic life, which was very chequered, with some serious personal problems, poor health, anti-semitism, and an unsatisfactory marriage to his lovely Alma. He had rheumatic fever when young, complicated by damage to heart valves, and indeed he eventually died, aged fifty-one years, from subacute bacterial endocarditis (SBE): a condition that in later years would be curable with penicillin. Mahler was somewhat of a hypochondriac. He gave quite detailed instructions for music conductors and players in his scores. He could not stand unnecessary noise.

Apparently, in relation to his 'Song of the Earth', he took up Buddhism.

Up to, and including his 5th Symphony, with its haunting, famous, beautiful adagio (used in the important film *Death in Venice*), Mahler appears to be searching for a spiritual existence.

The 6th, 7th and 8th symphonies have tragic themes. He appears to be particularly concerned with his own fate and impending doom. The last movement of his 6th symphony is very powerful, indeed almost over-whelming. It deals with death, including that of children. One of his own daughters had died in tragic circumstances, and Mahler had a long period of mourning. There are three quite alarming hammer blows of fate in the music of the 6th symphony. Mahler had become depressed, and he consulted Professor Sigmund Freud, the famous psychiatrist.

His massive 8th symphony was apparently composed when he had become extremely concerned about his beloved wife's infidelity, her close friendship with Gropius, the distinguished architect.

The 9th symphony is somewhat heartrending, with the awful fear of losing Alma. However, in that symphony there is also evidence of a desire to live and to work, in every possible way. It ends with joy, children playing in the sunlight.

He died before he could complete his 10th symphony.

Undoubtedly, Gustav Mahler had a major, lasting effect on music, overall. He never followed fashion.

Whilst living and working in Vienna, he became its most famous person.

Our musical interests and enjoyments are catholic. We like Mahler and Mozart, and some other classical composers, but in addition listen to Scott Joplin, 'real jazz', such as we heard in New Orleans, and music from several of the well known musical extravaganzas such as *Oklahoma* and indeed themes from such films as *Dr Zhivago* and *Lawrence of Arabia*. What would one do without music? When young, I enjoyed singing in the school choir, but cannot sing since I had a laryngeal tumour, many years ago.

CHAPTER 9

Epilogue

To see a world in a grain of sand
and a heaven in a wild flower
Hold infinity in the palm of your hand
An eternity in a hour

William Blake

I AGREE WITH THE CELEBRATED philosopher, Rousseau, who related in his book *Confessions* that he was puzzled by the fact that regarding memoirs, he must wait until he stopped thinking before he was able to begin.

Dear Sheelagh and Abby, I have done my best to carry out what I promised in the Preface of this book. I have provided a quite brief outline of a selected number of the vast and varied neurological disorders that may be encountered by a neurosurgeon, at least as were dealt with by me during my active time as one. No two people would have the same route to become such a specialist. In my case it has been possible to traverse the highways and by-ways to experience at first hand, and to get to know personally several distinguished people in the neurosciences in many countries; to be hosted by and to host a number of them whom we got to know. I was privileged to participate in conferences and seminars, and to be a guest lecturer or a visiting professor. Sheelagh accompanied me on most of my visits.

Although neurosurgery is a demanding, time consuming, but indeed fascinating and challenging surgical specialty, I have been fortunate in also being able to pursue some of my interests in extramural and non-governmental (NGO) fields.

The training of surgeons, including neurosurgeons, in recent times is quite different to that occurring in the days of the famous USA surgeon Halstead, with his graded autonomy; and also in my time, 'training' – mainly by apprenticeship. The arrangements and requirements have become much more stringent, organised and complex, a series of hurdles to be overcome for acceptance into a training scheme, hoping to be successful with the doctor's first choice of surgical specialty. There is monitoring and supervision, and careful assessments are made.

My upbringing was quite different, but I certainly agree that lifelong learning is essential. When I was a neurosurgical registrar, it was necessary to sleep overnight in a room which was actually in the ward, to be immediately available for critical patient care. An interesting training experience!

It was an honour and privilege to participate in the training over the years of many bright, keen young people, desirous of becoming medical or surgical neurologists, and then for me to follow their careers in their own countries.

We live in a time of unparalleled advances in medicine. Francis Bacon said, so many years ago, that: 'There is an insatiable desire for knowledge.' This desire remains. Before considering and putting into practice new developments and techniques, it is wise to be careful and sensibly cautious, but not to overdo this, before actually accepting them. I am reminded of the attitude of the Director of the USA Patent's Office in 1899, who stated that: 'Everything that has been invented, has been invented.' Also the statement of the famous Lord Kelvin: 'Radio has no future.' He also said: 'Heavier than air flying machines are impossible'!

To be pragmatic, when Einstein was asked: 'Why could men discover atoms, but not the means of controlling them?' he replied: 'That is simple, my friend. It is because politics is more difficult than physics.'

A sixteenth-century Chinese philosopher apparently found the future to be somewhat elusive. He said:

We seek it but cannot see it: we call it 'subtle',
We listen to it but cannot hear it: we call it 'essential',
We reach for it, but cannot grasp it: we call it 'serene'.

Two of my medical 'heroes' made interesting comments on ageism and scientific innovation: William Osler, the famous physician spoke of: 'The comparative weakness of man above 40 years. The vitalising work is done between the ages of 25 and 40, the anabolic or constructive period.' Wilder Penfield, the distinguished neurosurgeon, noted that: 'The writer who believes that he can describe the finally perfected surgical technique has entered the "fixed period" of his life; which is, or should be the signal for his retirement.'

I am aware of some of the developments in the neurosciences (the following is for medical doctors), from my readings and attendance at meetings. A major advance is the quite exciting development of endovascular imaging techniques, using flexible fibre and high resolution endoscopes. Thus, most cerebral aneurysms are treated by inserting a special coil into the aneurysm. Cerebral and spinal arterio-venous malformations are also being treated by this procedure, as are certain very vascular tumours. A stenosed carotid artery may be treated by inserting a stent or a balloon, rather than treatment by an endarterectomy. Stereotactic surgery has become more accurate, by using digital computation with computerised tomography and magnetic resonance imaging, giving direct visualisation of subcortical cerebral structures, also, better commercial electrodes have become available. There is a trend to carry out arthroplasty procedures, rather than bony fusion for certain cervical spine operations, but it would appear to be too soon to reliably evaluate the long term results. Apparently, gene therapy for cerebral gliomas is, so far, unsuccessful. Professor Bal Dhillon, Consultant ophthalmologist, informs me that proliferative diabetic retinopathy is treated nowadays by panretinal photocoagulation. There could be certain practical problems regarding the rapid developments of remarkable imaging techniques, possibly overtaking the ability of clinicians to accept the results and to put them promptly into practice. But they will catch up!

As in much of medicine, in neurosurgery new developments in investigations and therapies appear, are studied and considered carefully, and if accepted, are put into practice. This can sometimes involve changes in the actual work of neurosurgical departments. My example is that of the quite common and very important pathological condition of cerebral (intracranial) aneurysms. I mentioned this briefly earlier on in this book. There has been the important advent of radiological endovascular surgery carried out by highly trained Consultant neuroradiologists for the treatment of many, possibly now for most, of such aneurysms (indeed also for some arteriovenous anomalies, and some other vascular conditions seen in medical and surgical neurology). I presume that actual neurosurgical treatment by a craniotomy operation and the direct approach to such important, indeed potentially dangerous lesions, probably means that there is less 'hands on' work for some neurosurgeons, with dilution of the number of cases requiring treatment in their departments. I presume that there could be some problem of gaining and maintaining enough real experience.

Unfortunately, I am not up to date regarding such matters, but I would appreciate that doctors and other members of neurosurgical departments have dealt with the management of such important vascular disorders sensibly and reliably.

Stem cells are cells which have not yet been differentiated by the body to become specific body cells of many tissues, including the blood, nerves and organs. In Edinburgh, pioneering work is proceeding with the recently formed Scottish Centre for Regenerative Medicine (SCRM). There is the largest grouping of stem cell researches in the UK. It is internationally famous, and consists of more than twenty research groups. A better understanding of many diseases is being researched, leading to the development of new drugs and therapies. Could there possibly now be a real scientific approach for the early treatment of spinal cord injuried people?

The famous scientist Francis Crick said in his book *What Mad Pursuit*, that 'for at least several billion years, the double helix has been there, and active, and yet we are the first creatures on Earth to become aware of its existence.' In recent decades, remarkable biomedical advances have been and are being made concerning genome organisation and function, including studies on genomes and disease. Stem cells and genome researches will hopefully come into the domain of the management of several neurological diseases and injuries. Another remarkable development is that of nanotechnology. This would appear to be the dawn of a true scientific revolution in medicine, but has a long way to go. I understand that it would take 80,000 nanoparticles in a row to be just the diameter of a human hair. Apparently there could be earlier detection of disease, better drug therapies, and better targeting.

Success is something that we strive and aim for in our life. It requires hard work, determination and application. Several examples are mentioned in this book. There are various aspects of success, and a number of attributes; thus, having a wonderful family, a good life style, longevity, excellent employment, good friends, overcoming ill health, athletic prowess, and, being in control. I guess at times, 'a touch of serendipity', also!

Paul Getty gave a brief, simple answer when asked about success: 'My formula for success is – rise early, work late, and strike oil'!

But a more thoughtful and considered recipe for success was given by Kahlil Gibran:

And when you have reached the mountain top
Then you shall begin to climb
And when the earth shall claim your limbs
Then shall you truly dance.

The world has become more fragile, dangerous and complex, with wars and the activities of terrorists. One result must be the occurrence of many new casualties, and these will include combatants and civilians with serious neurological injuries: brain, spine, nerves, several with multiple injuries. I remember the words of our national poet, Robert Burns: 'Man's inhumanity to man, makes countless thousands mourn.'

I had the privilege and the pleasure of being educated as a schoolboy, then as a medical student, in the wonderful city of Edinburgh, the capital of glorious Scotland. I am most grateful to my endearing parents, to my family, to my dedicated teachers, my medical colleagues, and to the patients who permitted me to be their neurosurgeon.

I conclude with these thoughts:

Sitting quietly doing nothing
Spring comes and the grass grows by itself.

(Zen poem)

Great is the art of beginning; greater is the art of ending.

(Longfellow)

What a piece of work is man! how noble in reason! how infinite in faculties! in form and moving, how express and admirable! in action, how like an angel! in apprehension, how like a God! the beauty of the world! the paragon of animals! and yet, to me, what is this quintessence of dust? man delights not me; no, nor women either, though by your smiling you seem to say so.

(Shakespeare. Hamlet – Act ii Scene ii)

What a privilege I have had – to be a Neurosurgeon!

Appendices

42. *Major H. P. S. Aluwalia and the Prime Minister Mrs Indira Gandhi*

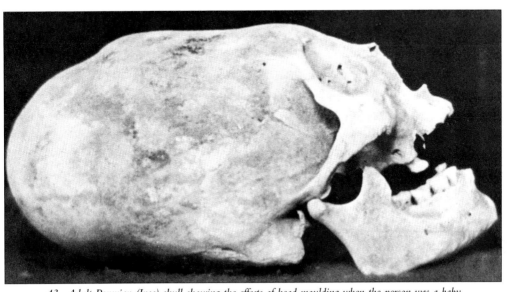

43. *Adult Peruvian (Inca) skull showing the effects of head moulding when the person was a baby*

44. *The Royal College of Surgeons of Edinburgh.* Courtesy of Royal College of Surgeons, Edinburgh

45. *The Duchess of Kent, honoured guest of the Rotary Club of Edinburgh, being presented with a Paul Harris award, the highest Rotary International award of Fellowship, Edinburgh 1992. She does wonderful work for several charities*

46. *Brigadier the Lord Ballantrae*

47. *International Conference on Recent Advances in Neurotraumatology (ICRAN), of the World Federation of Neurosurgical Societies (WFNS). Edinburgh 1982. Front: The Duke of Buccleuch. Behind: (left to right): Dr James Jenkinson (Secretary); myself; Professor William Luyendijk (Neurosurgeon) and Mr Douglas Crawford.*
Courtesy of Avril Anderson

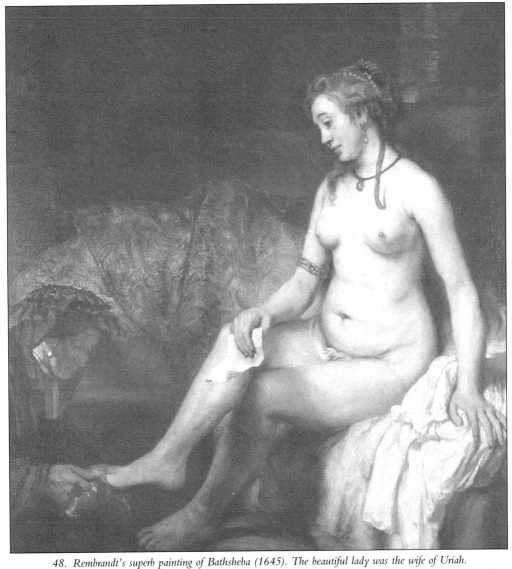

48. *Rembrandt's superb painting of Bathsheba (1645). The beautiful lady was the wife of Uriah.*
We are shown her washing herself, but she was spied by King David from the roof of his palace. He sent a message to her.
Rembrandt shows Bathsheba holding the letter. She went unto him (2 Samuel. Chapter XI).
This could be a major sexual comment in the history of art. (There is a suggestion in the painting that Bathsheba
has a tumour of the left breast.) The Bridgeman Art Gallery, London. Courtesy of Louvre, Paris

49. *Rembrandt: The Circumcision of Christ in the Stable* (1654)

50. Rembrandt: *Christ Disputing with Doctors*, 1654

51. Rembrandt: *The Golf Player*, 1654

Appointments

Several, including Consultant neurosurgeon, Department of Clinical Neurosciences, Western General Hospital, Edinburgh and Senior Lecturer in Neurosurgery, University of Edinburgh. 1953–87. Member of MRC Brain Metabolism Unit, University of Edinburgh. Captain RAMC Council Member (two occasions) Society of British Neurological Surgeons. Past-President of the British Cervical Spine Society. Past-Chairman of TRAB and PLAB. Founder, Chairman then Honorary President Scottish Disability Sport. Visiting Professor or Guest Lecturer in many countries.

Publications

Over 100, including these topics: cerebral aneurysms, head injuries, malignant cerebral gliomas, cervical spondylosis, hydrocephalus, spinal injuries, sport for disabled people, pituitary gland ablation, development and staffing of spinal units, intracranial hypertension, epilepsy, autonomic dysreflexia, and Rembrandt and Medicine, thrombosis of the internal carotid artery, uses for methyl methacrylate, spinal epidural haematoma, spinal subdural haematoma, *appareils electronique d'un special pour les grand impotents*, neurosurgical injuries from sport, cervical discography, treatment of acromegaly, cerebral paraplegia, intracranial hypertension, familial bovine epilepsy, and ataxia, spinal epidural abscess, a new absorbable bone sealant (Absele).

Books and chapters in books

Books: Spinal injuries; Head injuries; Epilepsy.
Chapters in Books; Head and brain – surgical anatomy; Surgical diathermy; Anterior approach to the cervical spine; The spine; Reconstructive surgery of the head; Advances in neuro-traumatology.

Medals and prizes

Medal of the International Spinal Cord Society; Medals for Demonstrating in Anatomy; The Dr A. S. Lakshimpathi Medal and Prize; The Clinical Surgery, Sir John Fraser Prize; Medals in Physiology, Physics, Midwifery and Gynaecology, Medicine and Surgery (School of Medicine, the three Royal Scottish Colleges).

Eponymous lectures

- Sydney Watson Smith Lecture. Royal College of Physicians of Edinburgh, 1968. 'Advances in the Investigation and Treatment of Cervical Spondylosis.'
- Honeymoon Gillespie Lecture. University of Edinburgh, 1968. 'Current Concepts in the Management of Brain Trauma.'

- The Dr A. S. Lakshimpathi Oration. Madras, India, 1986. 'The Use of Lasers in Medical and Surgical Practice.'
- The Donald Munro Memorial Lecture. American Paraplegia Society. Las Vegas, USA, 1990. 'Spinal Cord Injuries in the 21st Century.'

Honorary Member of medical learned societies

The American Association of Neurological Surgeons (AANS) (The Harvey Cushing Society).
The Hong Kong Surgical Society.
The Burmese Medical Association.
The Middle East Neurosurgical Society.
The Brazilian College of Surgeons.

Research grants

1. *The Captain H. Whitworth Research Fund* was given to me by that patient. The fund was controlled by the University of Edinburgh. It enabled me to (a) visit centres where epilepsy was being specially studied, in the Montreal Neurological Institute; and in Gothenburg, Sweden (depth electrode work). (b) Anterior cervical surgery, in UCLA, USA; and Hong Kong (Professor G. B. Ong, and Dr Fang).
2. *The MacRobert Trust Epilepsy Research Project.*
3. *ACMR Grant* to study and treat cervical spine intervertebral disc disorders.
4. *Research Grant from the Scottish Epilepsy Association* for the study of epilepsy.

Researches and innovations

Injuries sustained by Parachute Jumpers in Training (RAMC), Hip-cup arthroplasty (with Sir Walter Mercer); Cervical sympathectomy; Methyl methacrylate; Epilepsy; Pituitary gland ablation; Spinal units; Absele; Cervical disc disorders – anterior operative approach; Adjustable cervical spine bridge; Foam-plastic head and neck support; Sublingual glycerin trinitrate for autonomic dysreflexia.

Absele

Standard bone wax, made virtually to Sir Victor Horsley's original formula of 1892, continued to be used to control bleeding from the cut ends of bone during surgical operations ('dry as bone', that is, of living bone, is a misnomer!). The wax remains permanently and is a foreign body, and could therefore attract infection.

Experimental studies in the Ethicon laboratories produced a new bone sealant, which is absorbed with minimal tissue reaction in about three weeks. The substance is called 'Absele'. It is an absorbable haemostatic bone sealant, very easy to handle, which will permit good bone healing and does not interfere with callus formation. It is superior to bone wax. (Harris and Capperauld, 1978).

Methyl methacrylate

Methyl methacrylate is used surgically as a plastic type of material, to cover defects of the skull resulting from operations for a head injury or from disease, as an implant under the scalp.

I found two other uses for it:

(a) To securely fix part of the vertebral column which has become unstable due to trauma or disease, such as a neoplasm. At operation the affected part of the spine is exposed and methyl methacrylate, made up of the monomer (the fluid part), and the polymer (the powder) (to form a thick paste) is applied to the spine. It quickly sets and becomes quite hard.

I had the strength of the material tested in the laboratory of the Department of Engineering, Heriot Watt College (now, University), by Mr McBride.

(b) For sessile (no stalk or definite neck) cerebral aneurysms (small vascular berry or sac like abnormalities), that tend to rupture and seriously bleed, exposing the aneurysm at operation, and providing it with a safe, strong wrapping of small pieces of gauze dipped in methyl methacrylate (Harris, 1961).

Foam plastic head and neck splint

These were made for me, and consist of a curved piece of foam plastic in which the patient's neck lies, gripping the neck, with a flat piece of foam plastic attached to the curved portion, for the patient's head. Useful as a first aid measure, or during an operation on the front of the neck to restrict head and neck movements (Harris 1966).

An adjustable cervical spine bridge

This is a strong metal bridge for attachment to a Stryker Turning Frame. With the patient lying supine, his neck rests on the bridge and the height of this can be adjusted, for the management of certain cervical spine disorders, traumatic or non traumatic (Harris 1971).

Cerebral paraplegia

I noted that certain intracranial lesions, such as spasm (narrowing) of one or both anterior communicating arteries, from rupture of an aneurysm, or a localised brain injury or a neoplasm, involving the uppermost region of the cerebral hemispheres, can cause paraplegia. The term, 'cerebral paraplegia' was coined. Paper published in 1971.

Familial bovine ataxia and epilepsy

P. Harris et al. 1978.

Studies of muscle tone

- The use of torque generators to study clonus and disturbances of muscle tone. (Walsh and Harris, 1972).
- Simultaneous electrical and mechanical recording from postural muscles in a paraplegic patient (Walsh and Harris, 1972).

Classification of the clinical syndromes resulting from cervical disc degenerate disease

The likely response of certain of these syndromes to neurosurgical treatment.

New neurosurgical instruments

Designed and made for me in particular for anterior cervical spine surgery, including the trans-oral operation.

Recommendations for further reading

Ahluwalia, Major H.P.S. 1973. *Higher than Everest* (4th Edn. Vikas Publishing House, PVT Ltd. Delhi).

Anderson, Avril. 2004. *Douglas Crawford 1939–2002*. Tributes and Selected Writings.

Awad, I.A. 1995. *Philosophy of Neurological Surgery* (AANS Publishing Committee. American Association of Neurological Surgeons. Park Ridge, Ilinois).

Barclay, J.B. 1974. *The Tounis Scule. The Royal High School of Edinburgh* (RHS Club).

Bliss, Michael. 2006. *Harvey Cushing: A Life in Surgery* (Oxford Press).

Brain, Russell. 1959. *Science, Philosophy and Religion* (Cambridge University Press).

Cabiesis, Fernando. 1974. *Gods and Disease. Medicine in Ancient Peru* (Mediciones e Impressiones – Artegraf Jiros Quelia, Lima, Peru).

Critchley, Macdonald, Henson, R.A. 1977. *Music and the Brain* (William Heineman Medical Books Ltd.)

Dingwall, Helen M. 2005. *A Famous Flourishing Society: History of the Royal College of Surgeons 1500–2005* (Edinburgh University, Press).

Douglas M. Donald. 1969. *The Thoughtful Surgeon. James R. Learmonth* (University of Glasgow).

Fulton, John. 1946. *Harvey Cushing, A Biography* (Blackwell Ltd., Scientific Publications, Oxford).

Harris, Paul. 1987. *Edinburgh Since 1900* (Archive Publications Ltd. in association with Scotsman Publications Ltd, Edinburgh).

Harris, Phillip. 1963. *Spinal Injuries* (The Royal College of Surgeons, Edinburgh).

Harris, Phillip, & Mawdsley, Clifford. 1974. *Proceedings of the Hans Berger Centenary Symposium on Epilepsy* (Churchill Livingstone, Edinburgh).

Harris, Phillip. 1982. *Proceedings of the International Conference on Recent Advances in Neurotrauma (ICRAN)*, Edinburgh.

Jefferson, Geoffrey. 1941. Obituary of Otfried Foerster, *Lancet* ii. 503.

Mallard, J. R. 2006. 'The Contributions of Medical Physicists and Doctors in Aberdeen to the Evolution of Modern Medical Imaging: SPECT, PET and MRI. 1965–1992'. *Scot. Med. Journal* 51:44–48.

McIntyre, Iain & MacLarin, Iain, Eds. *Surgeons' Lives*, 2005. (Royal College of Surgeons of Edinburgh).

Mitchell, J.P., Lumb, G.N., Dobbie, A.K. 1978. *A Handbook of Surgical Diathermy*. P. Harris: Chapter X: 'Surgical Diathermy in Neurosurgery' (John Wright and Sons Ltd, Bristol).

Penfield, Wilder. 1977. *No Man Alone. A Neurosurgeon's Life* (Little, Brown & Co., Boston/Toronto).

Rengachary, S.S. & Ellenbogen, R.G., Eds. *Principles of Neurosurgery*, 2nd Edn. 2005 (Elsevier Mosby, Edinburgh).

Rentscher, Ingo, Herzberger, Barbara & Epstein, David. 1988. *Beauty and the Brain. Biological Aspects of Aesthetics* (Birkhauser, Verlag, Basel).

Ross, J.C. & Harris, P. 1980. 'A Tribute to Sir Ludwig Guttmann', *Paraplegia* 18: 153–6.

Rush, Christopher & Shaw, J.F. 1990. *With Sharp Compassion. Norman M. Dott* (Aberdeen University Press)

Sakula, Alexander. 1988. 'Selman Waksman (1888–1973). Discovery of Streptomycin: A Centenary Review'. *Brit. J. Dis. Chest.* 82: 23–31.

Schama, Simon. 1999. *Rembrandt's Eye* (Penguin Books Ltd., London).

Stem cells 27-04-07. An independent supplement from Mediaplanet About 'Stem Cells', distributed in *The Times* (newspaper) pages 1–11.

Whitteridge, David. 1983. 'Ludwig Guttmann 1899–1976'. *Biographies of Fellows of the Royal Society*. Vol. 29. Nov. 1983. 227.

References

Ashcroft, G., Townsend, H., McQueen, J.K. Harris, P. & Dow, R.C. 'Experimental epilepsy'. *J.Neurol.Neurosurg. Psychiat.* 1973. 36: 153.

Barlow, R.M., Dow, R.C., Harris P. et al. 'Familial bovine epilepsy and ataxia. Surgical technique for sampling cerebrospinal fluid, and for electrocorticography in cattle'. *Research in Vetin. Med.* 1978. 24: 358–65.

Cloward, R.B. 'The anterior approach for removal of ruptured cervical discs'. *J. Neurosurg.* 1958.15; 602–17.

Cullen, J.F., Harris, P., Gibson, P.S. et al. 'Pituitary gland ablation by Yttrium[90] implantation for advancing diabetic retinopathy. A further report'. *Brit. J. Ophthal.* 1971. 55 No.4. 217–24.

Forrest, A.P., Blair, D.W., Valentine, J.M. 'Screw implantation of the pituitary with Yttrium[90]. *Lancet* 1958. 26 July. 2: 192–3.

Harris, P. 'Head injuries in childhood'. *Arch. Dis. Childhood.* 1957. 32: 488.

Harris, P. & Udvarheyli, G. 'Aneurysms arising at the internal carotid artery – posterior communicating artery junction'. *J. Neurosurg.* 1957. 14: 180.

Harris, P. 'The uses of methyl methacrylate in neurosurgery: International Congress Series'. *Excerpta Medica.* 1961. 36.E81.

Harris, P. 'Chronic progressive communicating hydrocephalus due to protein transudates from brain and spinal tumours'. *Develop: Med. Child. Neurol.* 1962. 4: 56.

Harris, P. 'Head injuries resulting from sport'. *Bull. Brit. Assoc. Sport and Medicine.* 1965: 2: 1.

Harris, P. 'Foam plastic neck support'. *Brit. Med. J.* 1966: 2; 1006.

Harris, P. 'Advances in the investigation and treatment of cervical spondylosis'. Sydney Watson Smith Lecture. In the Symposium: Some aspects of Neurology. Ed. R. F. Robertson. *Roy. Coll. Physicians* Edinburgh. 1968. 38–50.

Harris, P. 'Strong A. J. Cerebral paraplegia'. Proc. 18th Annual Clinical Spinal Cord Injury Conference. Veterans Adminstration, Harvard Medical School, Boston. 1971. 21–4.

Harris, P. 'Adjustable cervical bridge'. *Brit. Med. J.* 1971.168.

Harris, P. & Walsh, E.G. 'The use of torque generators to study clonus and disturbance of muscle tone'. *Paraplegia.* 1972. 9.4.228.

Harris, P. & Walsh, E.G. ' Simultaneous electrical and mechanical recording from postural muscles'. *Paraplegia*. 1972. 9.4.229.

Harris, P. & Capperauld, I. 'A new absorbable haemostatic bone sealant'. *J. Roy. Coll. Surg. Edin.* 1978. 23: 285–91.

Harris P. 'Anterior approach to the cervical discs'. Chapter in *Operative Surgery –Neurosurgery*. Ed. L. Symon. 4th Edn. 1989. Vol.14. (Butterworth and Co., London) 381–95.

Harris, P. 'Cervical spine stenosis'. *Paraplegia* 1977 Aug. 125–32. Increased knowledge of the anatomy, physiology and biomechanics of the cervical spine and the enclosed neural and vascular elements is leading to a better understanding of the importance of cervical spine stenosis, as certain clinical syndromes may ensue and may respond well to operative decompression. The present study was designed to investigate the incidence of cervical spine stenosis in patients who have required surgical treatment for cervical spondylosis and to evaluate the clinical results.

Harris, P. 'Rembrandt and Medicine'. *J. Roy. Coll. Surg. Edin.* 1994. 81–3.

Harris, P. 'Self-induced autonomic dysreflexia practised by some tetraplegic athletes to enhance their athletic performances'. *Paraplegia* 1994. 32: 289–91.

Harris, P. 'Spinal cord injuries in the 21st century'. The Donald Munro Memorial Lecture. *Proc. Amer. Paraplegia Soc. New York.* April 1990: 1–30.

Harris, P. 'Stab wound of the back causing an acute spinal subdural haematoma with a Brown-Sequard syndrome'. *Spinal Cord.* 2004. 43: 678.

Heimlich, H. J. 'The Heimlich Maneouvre'. *Brit. Med. J.* 1983: 286. 1349–50.

Jennett, B. & Plum, F. 'Persistent vegetative state after brain damage'. *Lancet* 1972. April. 734–7.

La Londe, A.A. & Gardner, W.J. ' Chronic subdural haematoma: expansion of the compressed cerebral hemispheres and relief of hypertension by spinal injection of physiological saline solution'. *New Eng. J. Med.* 1948. 239; 293–6.

McQueen, J.R., Blackwood, P.H.R., Harris, P. et al. 'Low risk of late post-traumatic seizures following severe head injury: implications for clinical trials of prophylaxis'. *J. Neurol. Neurosurg. Psychiat.* 1983. 46: 899–904. Trial Director: P. Harris.

Murray, J. *A history of the Royal High School.* The Royal High School Club, Edinburgh 1997.

Robinson, R.A. & Smith, G.W. 'Antero-lateral disc removal and interbody fusion for cervical disc syndrome'. Bull. John Hopkins Hospital. 1955. 9. 223.

Wiltberger, E.R. 'The prefit dowel intervertebral body fusion as used in lumbar disc surgery'. *Amer J. Surg.* 1953. 86: 723.

Glossary

Simple explanations of some medical terms

It is hoped that much of this book will be meaningful to both medical doctors and to a number of intelligent lay people. For the latter, I am providing a simple explanation of the meaning of certain of the medical terms; such readers could also obtain further elucidation from their own medical doctors.

ablation:	destruction.
adenoma:	a solid, definable mass of cells (see section on the pituitary).
ala of the nose:	the soft fleshy part.
amnesic:	loss of memory.
anterior cervical spine operation:	(see chapter on the Spine, degenerative diseases).
anterolateral cordotomy:	(see chapter on the Spine, section on the Surgical Treatment of Pain).
arterial spasm:	narrowing of an artery from significant mechanical irritation of the vessel.
arteriovenous lesion:	(vascular malformation) (see chapter on Brain: cerebro-vascular disorders).
ataxia:	loss of balance.
atlanto-axial region:	the uppermost part of the cervical spine. The atlas is the first cervical vertebra, and the axis the second.
atheromatous:	degenerative – diseased area of an artery.
aura:	a premonitory symptom experienced by the patient.
autonomic:	self-governing.

benign:	not malignant; is located in one area and does not metastasise (spread to other regions).
bipolar coagulation:	(see item on haemostasis).
burr-hole:	a small hole drilled in the skull.
cauda equina:	several lumbar, and all of the sacral spinal nerves, in adults, come off the tail end of the spinal cord – which ends at lumbar one-two level, forming the cauda equina (horse's tail) in the spinal canal.
cauda equina claudication:	compression of these nerve roots in a narrowed (stenosed) lumbar spinal canal, causing acute pains in the legs when walking and becoming progressively worse when walking shorter and shorter distances.
cerebellum:	the postero-inferior part of the brain, mainly concerned with balance.
cerebral aneurysm:	(see item in chapter on Brain: cerebrovascular disorders)
cerebral angiography:	visualisation of the intracranial vessels (arteries, veins and venous sinuses) by injecting a radio-opaque fluid into an artery in the neck and taking X-rays.
cerebrospinal fluid:	(CSF) the clear, watery like fluid produced in the ventricles of the brain, under pressure, which courses down to the fourth ventricle, escaping into the subarachnoid space surrounding the brain and the spinal cord. The CSF is then absorbed into, mainly, the superior longitudinal venous sinus situated at the top of the brain, and thence into the main vascular system.
cervical spine:	the part of the spine (vertebral column) in the neck, between the base of the skull above, and below, the thoracic part of the spine.
cervical spondylosis:	degenerative changes in the cervical spine causing bony ridges, and narrowing of the spinal canal. They are called osteophytes.

cisterna magna:	the enlarged subarachnoid space (cistern) located in the postero-inferior aspect of the skull.
coagulation:	sealing off of a bleeding vessel, using a diathermy machine.
cognitive:	the action of faculty of knowing.
cog-wheel spasticity:	repeated slight jerky 'jumps' with passive movements of the joints of limbs; being carried out by a clinical examiner. Spasticity – some resistance to the flexion of limb joints.
communicating hydrocephalus:	where there is full communication between the ventricular system and the subarachnoid space. *Non-communicating hydrocephalus*: the CSF cannot escape from the ventricular system.
congenital:	born with an abnormality.
contractures:	flexion deformities of limbs, or parts of them e.g. the wrists and hands, due to disease of the tissues around joints, resulting in, usually, marked flexion contractures.
convulsions:	fits.
cranial sutures:	the junctions (joints) of the skull bones.
craniotomy:	the surgeon temporarily removes part of the skull, to gain access to the brain, and replaces the bone (skull flap) at the end of the operation.
cryosurgery:	a surgical technique using frozen nitrous oxide gas, to destroy certain abnormal tissues.
cystic change:	a cavity inside a tumour.
decerebration:	absence of function of the higher centres of the brain.
decompressive laminectomy:	surgical removal of the posterior aspect of part of the vertebral column.
deep reflexes:	tapping (with a rubber 'hammer') the tendons (muscles become tendons) at the elbows, and wrists, knees and ankles, producing, normally, jerking of the limb distal to tendon. In certain

neurological disorders they may be absent or exaggerated.

dermatome:　the area of skin supplied by a nerve carrying sensation; tested by using a pin, and then, also, a wisp of cotton wool or paper.

diathermise:　to accurately destroy a limited part of the brain using coagulation.

dissecting microscope:　a special microscope used by the surgeon to magnify and illuminate very brightly the region of the brain being operated on. (Can also be used for operations in other body regions).

doll's eye testing:　this will be familiar to neurologists, both medical and surgical. It is a simple quick clinical test to determine the integrity or otherwise of a patient's brainstem.

dorsal columns:　are the nerve fibres (tracts) situated one on each side of the posterior (dorsal) aspect of the spinal cord.

drop attacks:　sudden, usually brief episode where the patient loses power in his/her trunk and falls.

electroencephalogram:　a special technique to sample and record the electrical changes on and in the brain (the 'brain waves'). Special small electrodes (receivers) made of metal are placed on the patient's scalp (EEG), or in the brain, in predetermined locations (ECOG). Then the wires from the electrodes are attached to an electroencephalograph machine, to record the brain (cerebral) activity. Various pathological changes may be studied, and in particular, 'the epilepsies'. All of us with normal brains would show the normal alpha waves on an EEG study.

electro-neurophysiological studies:　techniques to study the 'brain waves' (the electro-encephalogram (EEG); also to study functions of nerves, by nerve conduction tests.

embolus:　'a free agent' travelling in a vessel – an artery or a vein. Can be a portion of blood clot; or part of a diseased area, an atheromatous plaque in an artery, or tumour cells, fat, air or blood.

endovascular technique: a technique, usually carried out by skilled neuroradiologists, to pass a fine instrument up the arterial system from the artery in the groin (femoral), to reach intracranially, and then enable appropriate treatment to deal with certain vascular abnormalities, mainly aneurysms and arteriovenous malformations.

eosinophil and basophil: terms denoting how the tumour (adenoma) responds to certain dyes – studied by neuro-pathologists.

expressive dysphasia: difficulty in speaking, because of brain lesion in the speech area.

extensor reflex: stroking the sole of the feet normally results in flexion of the big toe; if extension of that toe results this is abnormal.

extradural haematoma: a quantity of blood situated between the dura (outer covering of the brain and the spinal cord) and the brain, usually from a head injury causing a skull-fracture, tearing the artery running in the temporal-bone, causing compression of the brain (or spinal cord).

facet joints: these are small bony plates on each side of a vertebra, two above and two below, forming articulations (joints) with the vertebrae above and below. They are synovial joints, lined by a shiny membrane.

fallopian tube: the two tubes in the female pelvis which receive eggs from the ovary and transmit them to the uterus (womb).

fasciculations: visible flickering movements of parts of muscles under the skin. Usually indicating significant damage of the nerve(s) supplying the muscle(s).

femoral nerve stretch test: patient prone (that is, face down); the leg is then extended at the hip, and the test is positive if the patient now experiences pain in the front of the thigh.

fontanelle:	the strong layer of tissue between the anterior bones of a baby's skull.
frozen section biopsy:	a specimen of tissue, for example from a brain tumour, taken during an operation, is processed by a pathologist. This includes freezing and staining the tissue and using a microscope. The result of the very quick study is then given directly to the neurosurgeon in the operating theatre, allowing him then to decide what neurosurgical treatment is required.
Gardner-Wells skull tongs:	a metal hoop with special spring loaded points which secures the apparatus to the head. Then traction can be safely applied with a cord and weights, for example, to reduce a dislocation of the cervical spine.
glossopharyngeal:	this is the ninth cranial nerve. It supplies sensation to most of the tongue, and the posterior part of the mouth.
Guillain Barre Syndrome:	an acute peripheral nerve involvement, with loss of motor power.
haemophilia:	a bleeding disorder.
haemostasis:	stopping of bleeding (haemorrhage).
hemianopia:	partial loss of vision in a patient's visual field (the visual field is all that we normally see with an eye).
hemiparesis:	partial paralysis of one half of the body, possibly including sensation, visual and speech disturbances.
hemiplegia:	complete hemiparesis.
hemi-spinal cord neurological deficit:	a lesion involving the nerve tracts in one half of the spinal cord. Has the eponym: Brown-Sequard syndrome.
histology:	the examination of diseased tissue under a microscope.
hyperaesthesia:	an increased feeling of sensation (to clinical testing).
hypoaesthesia:	depressed loss of sensation.

hypopituitarism:	too little of the pituitary hormones being produced.
hypotension:	lowering the blood pressure.
idiopathic:	no obvious cause.
imaging study:	includes conventional X-rays, contrast X-rays, angiograms, CT (computed tomography) and MRI (magnetic resonance imaging).
infarction:	lack of a proper blood supply to, in this case, the brain, which 'dies' and loses function.
intrathecally:	injection of a drug directly into subarachnoid spaces (usually in the lower (lumbar) spinal region).
ischaemic:	reduction of the normal blood supply.
Jacksonian:	named after Hughlings Jackson, a famous medical neurologist. A form of epilepsy characterised by usually limited involuntary jerking movements of part of one side of the body. The patient is usually conscious.
kyphoscoliosis:	a deformity of the vertebral column.
laminectomy:	operative removal of laminae, the sheets of bone being, with the bony spinal processes (midline), the posterior parts of the vertebrae.
larynx:	the 'voice box', includes the vocal cords.
ligamentum flavum:	the yellow tough tissue (ligament) which joins the posterior parts of the vertebrae together.
lumbar:	the five (lumbar) vertebrae in the lower part of the back. Beyond (caudal) there is the sacrum, and superiorly (cranially) are the 12 thoracic vertebrae –above them are the 7 cervical vertebrae.
lumbar puncture:	a needle is inserted posteriorly into, usually, the lumbar subarachnoid space.
materia medica:	the remedial substances used in medicine.
Mayfield aneurysm clips:	metallic spring clips used during a cranial operation to clip – occlude – the neck of an aneurysm.

Mayfield head clamp:	this is securely fixed to the patient's head at the beginning of a cranial operation, to prevent any movement of the head during the operation.
medulla:	the spinal cord.
metastatic:	a tumour (malignant) spreading to other parts of the body.
mid-thoracic protrusion:	see item on *intervertebral disc protrusions.*
myelopathy:	a pathological degenerative change in the spinal cord.
neural tube:	the name for the embryonic, developing spinal cord and nerves.
NHND:	National Hospital for Nervous Diseases.
oncologist:	a medical doctor specialising in the treatment of malignant tumours, usually by deep X-ray therapy, or/and chemotherapy.
optic chiasm:	the inner parts of the optic (eye) nerves cross over to the opposite side, whereas the outer parts do not. This forms in what is termed 'the optic chiasm'. These fibres then extend backwards, to the distal part of the brain, the occipital lobe.
osteophytes:	are bony (arthritic) spurs or (excrescences) of the edges of bones, adjacent to joints.
palliative:	mitigating or temporarily relieving diseased tissues.
papilloedema:	swelling of the optic disc (visual nerve head), usually indicating raised intracranial pressure. Diagnosed by using an ophthalmoscope.
pathology:	the study of diseased tissues and organs.
PBB Hospital:	Peter Bent Brigham Hospital
photophobia:	unpleasant reaction to light.
phrenic nerves:	the two nerves that supply the diaphragm (the largest muscle in the body).
pituitary gland:	(see item in chapter on Brain: intracranial neoplasms).

position sense:	is tested by moving a toe or finger (etc) up or down; patient's eyes closed; asked to give an answer 'which way?'
post-herpetic neuralgia:	intractable burning pain felt in the site of the skin rash of the herpes zoster (shingles)
post-partum:	after birth of a child.
Pott's paraplegia:	paraplegia named after Percival Pott. Most likely causing curvature of the spine due to tuberculosis.
prosthesis:	an item, metal or non-metal, to supply deficiencies, for example an artificial joint.
pyramidal:	pertaining to the motor tracts in the nervous system; concerned with motor functions of muscles.
radiculopathy:	involvement of a nerve root (or roots) with resulting symptoms and signs pertaining to the tissues (muscles, skin etc) supplied by that nerve.
receptive dysphasia:	difficulty in understanding someone's speech because of a brain lesion in the speech area.
safe areas of the brain:	areas outwith the locations of definite regions, such as speech, motor, sensory, visual.
SBNS:	Society of British Neurological Surgeons.
segments:	dermatomes – that is the area of skin corresponding to the supply of a spinal nerve.
seminoma:	one type of tumour of the testicle.
sequestration:	a free portion of a damaged intervertebral disc, shorn off by the injury to the spine.
sphincter disturbance:	abnormal function of the urinary bladder or/and the bowels.
spina bifida occulta:	the failure of normal closure of the posterior part of the vertebral column. Usually the thoraco-lumbar region of the spine.
spino-thalamic tracts:	are nerve fibres (tracts) in the spinal cord, transmitting the sensations of pain, touch, temperature and indeed tickle from the skin up the spinal cord to a deep structure in the brain – the

thalamus, thence on to appropriate areas of the brain, to reach consciousness of the individual. These tracts cross over during their transit in the spinal cord.

stent: a special splint introduced into a diseased artery to obtain and retain the calibre (diameter) of the artery.

Stryker Turning frame: consists of a metal frame which has fittings so that a patient's head and neck may be put on traction using metal tongs (such as the Gardner-Wells skull tongs) fixed to the patient's head; then a cord is attached and is passed over a pulley and weights are attached, to reduce cervical spine dislocations or subluxations. There is a mirror image of the frame, so that the patient can be easily turned, when required, by nursing staff.

subdural haematoma: a clot of blood located beneath the strong covering of the brain, the dura, compressing the underlying brain.

subluxation: incomplete dislocation.

superior longitudinal sinus: a large vein-like structure, situated in the uppermost central part of the brain, receiving the venous blood draining from the main part of the cerebral (brain) hemispheres.

sympathectomy: with loss of sensation of the cornea of the eye and the ala of the nose, ulceration may develop. These can be cured by dividing the sympathetic nerve in the neck, a sympathectomy.

temporalis muscle: is in the temporal region, just above the (external; pinna) ear.

tetraparesis: partial tetraplegia.

tetraplegia: motor paralysis and loss of sensation in all four limbs and the trunk, also of the urinary bladder; bowels, sexual organs, and of respiration.

thermo-analgesia: reduction of temperature sensation, usually also of pain and touch sensation.

thrombo-arteritis:	inflammation of arteries.
thrombophlebitis:	inflammation and thrombosis (clotting) of veins.
thrombosis:	solid clot of blood in a vessel, usually an artery.
tracheostomy:	a surgical opening in the trachea (wind-pipe) and insertion of a special (tracheostomy) tube, to assist breathing, which may require to be connected to a respirator.
trans-oral:	through the patient's mouth, to reach the anterior aspect of the uppermost region of the cervical spine.
transphenoidal approach:	a neurosurgical approach to the pituitary fossa (gland region), by a procedure through the nose-region, and the air cavity (sinus beyond, then entering the pituitary (gland) fossa).
transient:	brief.
trigeminal ganglion:	the 3 branches (TRI – three) of the 5th cranial nerve, ophthalmic supplying the forehead and the cornea of the eye, the maxillary the middle of the face and upper gums and lip, and the mandibular – the chin and lower gums and lip. The branches enter the skull, being incorporated in the trigeminal ganglion – from there on to the thalamus and then onto a part of the brain where sensations reach consciousness.
tuberculomas:	a well defined mass (like a small ball) of tuberculous and adjacent cerebral (brain) tissue.
VA:	Veterans Administration (USA).
ventriculography:	injection of air into the cavities (the ventricles) inside the brain to outline them, as will be seen in X-rays. Will help to define certain pathologies, such as a brain tumour.

Index of People

Bold type indicates illustration numbers

Subject Index